THE
AYN RAND
SAMPLER

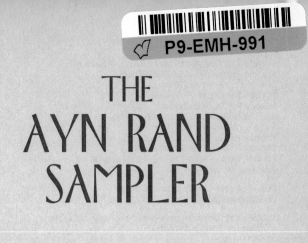

SIGNET
Published by New American Library, a division of
Penguin Putnam Inc., 375 Hudson Street,
New York, New York 10014, U.S.A.
Penguin Books Ltd, 80 Strand,
London WC2R 0RL, England
Penguin Books Australia Ltd, Ringwood,
Victoria, Australia
Penguin Books Canada Ltd, 10 Alcorn Avenue,
Toronto, Ontario, Canada M4V 3B2
Penguin Books (N.Z.) Ltd, 182–190 Wairau Road,
Auckland 10, New Zealand

Penguin Books Ltd, Registered Offices:
Harmondsworth, Middlesex, England

Published by Signet, an imprint of New American Library,
a division of Penguin Putnam Inc.

First Printing, August 2002
10 9 8 7 6 5 4 3 2 1

Printed in the United States of America

PUBLISHER'S NOTE FOR FICTION SELECTIONS
Names, characters, places, and incidents either are the product of the
author's imagination or are used fictitiously, and any resemblance to
actual persons, living or dead, business establishments, events, or locales
is entirely coincidental.

CONTENTS

Introduction   v

Fiction Selections   1

The Fountainhead
"Roark and the Dean"   2

Atlas Shrugged
"The John Galt Line"   19
"The Meaning of Money"   50

Nonfiction Selections   54

The Romantic Manifesto
"The Goal of My Writing"   54

The Virtue of Selfishness
"Man's Rights"   65

Ayn Rand's Books   73

Biography   95

Recollections of Ayn Rand   97

INTRODUCTION

by Leonard Peikoff

Ayn Rand is one of America's favorite authors. In a recent Library of Congress/Book of the Month Club survey, American readers ranked *Atlas Shrugged*—her masterwork—as second only to the Bible in its influence on their lives. For decades, at scores of college campuses around the country, students have formed clubs to discuss the works of Ayn Rand. In 1998, the Oscar-nominated *Ayn Rand: A Sense of Life*, a documentary film about her life, played to sold-out venues throughout America and Canada. In recognition on her enduring popularity, the United States Postal Service in 1999 issued an Ayn Rand stamp.

Every book by Ayn Rand published in her lifetime is still in print, and hundreds of thousands of copies of them are sold every year, so far totaling more then twenty million. Why?

Ayn Rand understood, all the way down to fundamentals, why man needs the unique form of nourishment that is literature. And she provided a banquet that was at once intellectual and thrilling.

The major novels of Ayn Rand contain superlative values that are unique in our age. *Atlas Shrugged* (1957) and *The Fountainhead* (1943) offer profound and original philosophic themes, expressed in logical, dramatic plot structures. They portray an uplifted vision of man, in the form of protagonists characterized by strength, purposefulness, integrity—heroes who are not only idealists, but happy idealists, self-confident, serene, at home on earth. (See synopses later in this sampler.)

Ayn Rand's first novel, *We the Living* (1936), set in the post-revolutionary Soviet Union, is an indictment not merely of Soviet-style Communism, but of any and every totalitarian state that claims the right to sacrifice the supreme value of an individual human life.

Anthem (1946), a prose poem set in the future, tells of one man's rebellion against an utterly collectivized world, a world in which joyless, selfless men are permitted to exist only for the sake of serving the group. Written in 1937, *Anthem* was first published in England; it was refused publication in American until 1946, for reasons the reader can discover by reading it for himself.

Ayn Rand wrote in a highly calculated literary style intent on achieving precision and luminous clarity, yet that style is at the same time colorful, sensuously evocative, and passionate.

Her exalted vision of man and her philosophy for living on earth, Objectivism, have changed the lives of tens of thousands of readers and launched a major philosophic movement with a growing impact on American culture.

You are invited to enjoy the selections from Ayn Rand's philosophical writings and novels in this sampler. I hope you enjoy them as much as I have.

FICTION SELECTIONS

The Fountainhead

The Fountainhead *(1943) introduced the world to architect Howard Roark, an intransigent, egoistic hero of colossal stature. A man whose arrogant pride in his work is fully earned, Roark is an innovator who battles against a tradition-worshipping society. Expelled from a prestigious architectural school, refused work, reduced to laboring in a granite quarry, Roark is never stopped. He has to withstand not merely professional rejection, but also the enmity of Ellsworth Toohey, leading humanitarian; of Gail Wynand, powerful publisher; and of Dominique Francon, the beautiful columnist who loves him fervently yet, for reasons you will discover, is bent on destroying his career.*

At the climax of the novel, the untalented but successful architect Peter Keating, a college friend of his, pleads with Roark for help in designing a prestigious project that Roark himself wanted but was too unpopular to win. Roark agrees to design the project secretly on condition that it be built strictly according to his drawings. During construction, however, Roark's building is thoroughly mutilated. Having no recourse in law, Roark takes matters into his own hands in a famous act of dynamiting. In the process and the subsequent courtroom trial, he makes his stand clear, risking his career, his love, and his life.

The Fountainhead *portrays individualism versus collectivism, not in politics, but in man's soul; it presents the motivations and the basic premises that produce the character of an individualist or a collectivist.*

The Fountainhead *was made into a motion picture in 1949, starring Gary Cooper and Patricia Neal, for which*

AR wrote the screenplay. The movie, available on video, often plays on cable TV and at art-house cinemas, where it is always received enthusiastically.

Roark and the Dean

Howard Roark laughed.

He stood naked at the edge of a cliff. The lake lay far below him. A frozen explosion of granite burst in flight to the sky over motionless water. The water seemed immovable, the stone—flowing. The stone had the stillness of one brief moment in battle when thrust meets thrust and the currents are held in a pause more dynamic than motion. The stone glowed, wet with sunrays.

The lake below was only a thin steel ring that cut the rocks in half. The rocks went on into the depth, unchanged. They began and ended in the sky. So that the world seemed suspended in space, an island floating on nothing, anchored to the feet of the man on the cliff.

His body leaned back against the sky. It was a body of long straight lines and angles, each curve broken into planes. He stood, rigid, his hands hanging at his sides, palms out. He felt his shoulder blades drawn tight together, the curve of his neck, and the weight of the blood in his hands. He felt the wind behind him, in the hollow of his spine. The wind waved his hair against the sky. His hair was neither blond nor red, but the exact color of ripe orange rind.

He laughed at the thing which had happened to him that morning and at the things which now lay ahead.

He knew that the days ahead would be difficult. There were questions to be faced and a plan of action to be prepared. He knew that he should think about it. He knew also that he would not think, because everything was clear to him already, because the plan had been set long ago, and because he wanted to laugh.

He tried to consider it. But he forgot. He was looking at the granite.

He did not laugh as his eyes stopped in awareness of the earth around him. His face was like a law of nature—a thing one could not question, alter or implore. It had high cheekbones over gaunt, hollow cheeks; gray eyes, cold and steady; a contemptuous mouth shut tight, the mouth of an executioner or a saint.

He looked at the granite. To be cut, he thought, and made into walls. He looked at a tree. To be split and made into rafters. He looked at a streak of rust on the stone and thought of iron ore under the ground. To be melted and to emerge as girders against the sky.

These rocks, he thought, are here for me; waiting for the drill, the dynamite and my voice; waiting to be split, ripped, pounded, reborn; waiting for the shape my hands will give them.

Then he shook his head, because he remembered that morning and that there were many things to be done. He stepped to the edge, raised his arms, and dived down into the sky below.

He cut straight across the lake to the shore ahead. He reached the rocks where he had left his clothes. He looked regretfully about him. For three years, ever since he had lived in Stanton, he had come here for his only relaxation, to swim, to rest, to think, to be alone and alive, whenever he could find one hour to spare, which had not been often. In his new freedom the first thing he wanted to do was to come here, because he knew that he was coming for the last time. That morning he had been expelled from the Architectural School of the Stanton Institute of Technology.

He pulled his clothes on: old denim trousers, sandals, a shirt with short sleeves and most of its buttons missing. He swung down a narrow trail among the boulders, to a path running through a green slope, to the rode below.

He walked swiftly, with a loose, lazy expertness of motion. He walked down the long road, in the sun. Far ahead Stanton lay sprawled on the coast of Massachusetts, a little town as a setting for the gem of its existence—the great Institute rising on a hill beyond.

The township of Stanton began with a dump. A gray mound of refuse rose in the grass. It smoked faintly. Tin cans glittered in the sun. The road led past the first houses to a church. The church was a Gothic monument of shingles painted pigeon blue. It had stout wooden buttresses supporting nothing. It had stained-glass windows with heavy traceries of imitation stone. It opened the way into long streets edged by tight, exhibitionist lawns. Behind the lawns stood wooden piles tortured out of all shape: twisted into gables, turrets, dormers; bulging with porches; crushed under huge, sloping roofs. White curtains floated at the windows. A garbage can stood at a side door, flowing over. An old Pekinese sat upon a cushion on a doorstep, its mouth drooling. A line of diapers fluttered in the wind between the columns of a porch.

People turned to look at Howard Roark as he passed. Some remained staring after him with sudden resentment. They could give no reason for it: it was an instinct his presence awakened in most people. Howard Roark saw no one. For him, the streets were empty. He could have walked there naked without concern.

He crossed the heart of Stanton, a broad green edged by shop windows. The windows displayed new placards announcing: WELCOME TO THE CLASS OF '22! GOOD LUCK, CLASS OF '22! The Class of '22 of the Stanton Institute of Technology was holding its commencement exercises that afternoon.

Roark swung into a side street, where at the end of a long row, on a knoll over a green ravine, stood the house of Mrs. Keating. He had boarded at that house for three years.

Mrs. Keating was out on the porch. She was feeding a couple of canaries in a cage suspended over the railing. Her pudgy little hand stopped in mid-air when she saw him. She watched him with curiosity. She tried to pull her mouth into a proper expression of sympathy; she succeeded only in betraying that the process was an effort.

He was crossing the porch without noticing her. She stopped him.

"Mr. Roark!"

"Yes?"

"Mr. Roark, I'm so sorry about—" she hesitated demurely, "—about what happened this morning."

"What?" he asked.

"Your being expelled from the Institute. I can't tell

you how sorry I am. I only want you to know that I feel for you."

He stood looking at her. She knew that he did not see her. No, she thought, it was not that exactly. He always looked straight at people and his damnable eyes never missed a thing, it was only that he made people feel as if they did not exist. He just stood looking. He would not answer.

"But what I say," she continued, "is that if one suffers in this world, it's on account of error. Of course, you'll have to give up the architect profession now, won't you? But then a young man can always earn a decent living clerking or selling or something."

He turned to go.

"Oh, Mr. Roark!" she called.

"Yes?"

"The Dean phoned for you while you were out."

For once, she expected some emotion from him; and an emotion would be the equivalent of seeing him broken. She did not know what it was about him that had always made her want to see him broken.

"Yes?" he asked.

"The Dean," she repeated uncertainly, trying to recapture her effect. "The Dean himself through his secretary."

"Well?"

"She said to tell you that the Dean wanted to see you immediately the moment you got back."

"Thank you."

"What do you suppose he can want *now*?"

"I don't know."

He had said: "I don't know." She had heard distinctly: "I don't give a damn." She stared at him incredulously.

"By the way," she said, "Petey is graduating today." She said it without apparent relevance.

"Today? Oh, yes."

"It's a great day for me. When I think of how I skimped and slaved to put my boy through school. Not that I'm complaining. I'm not one to complain. Petey's a brilliant boy."

She stood drawn up. Her stout little body was corseted to tightly under the starched folds of her cotton dress that it seemed to squeeze the fat out to her wrists and ankles.

"But of course," she went on rapidly, with the eagerness of her favorite subject, "I'm not one to boast. Some mothers are lucky and others just aren't. We're all in our rightful place. You just watch Petey from now on. I'm not one to want my boy to kill himself with work and I'll thank the Lord for any small success that comes his way. But if that boy isn't the greatest architect of this U.S.A., his mother will want to know the reason why!"

He moved to go.

"But what am I doing, gabbing with you like that!" she said brightly. "You've got to hurry and change and run along. The Dean's waiting for you."

She stood looking after him through the screen door, watching his gaunt figure move across the rigid neatness of her parlor. He always made her uncomfortable in the house, with a vague feeling of apprehension, as if she were waiting to see him swing out suddenly and smash her coffee tables, her Chinese vases, her framed photographs. He had never shown any inclination to do so. She kept expecting it, without knowing why.

Roark went up the stairs to his room. It was a large, bare room, made luminous by the clean glow of whitewash. Mrs. Keating had never had the feeling that Roark really lived there. He had not added a single object to the bare necessities of furniture which she had provided; no pictures, no pennants, no cheering human touch. He had brought nothing to the room but his clothes and his drawings; there were few clothes and too many drawings; they were stacked high in one corner; sometimes she thought that the drawings lived there, not the man.

Roark walked now to these drawings; they were the first things to be packed. He lifted one of them, then the next, then another. He stood looking at the broad sheets.

They were sketches of buildings such as had never stood on the face of the earth. They were as the first houses built by the first man born, who had never heard of others building before him. There was nothing to be said of them, except that each structure was inevitably what it had to be. It was not as if the draftsman had sat over them, pondering laboriously, piecing together doors, windows and columns, as his whim dictated and as the books prescribed. It was as if the buildings had sprung from the earth and from some living force, complete, unalterably right. The hand that had made the sharp pencil lines still had much to learn. But not a line seemed superfluous, not a needed plane was missing. The structures were austere and simple, until one looked at them and realized what work, what complexity of method, what tension of thought had achieved the simplicity. No laws had dictated a single detail. The buildings were not Classical, they were not Gothic, they were not Renaissance. They were only Howard Roark.

He stopped, looking at a sketch. It was one that had never satisfied him. He had designed it as an exercise he had given himself, apart from his schoolwork; he did that often when he found some particular site and stopped before it to think of what building it should bear. He had spent nights staring at this sketch, wondering what he had missed. Glancing at it now, unprepared, he saw the mistake he had made.

He flung the sketch down on the table, he bent over it, he slashed lines straight through his neat drawing. He stopped once in a while and stood looking at it, his fingertips pressed to the paper; as if his hands held the building. His hands had long fingers, hard veins, prominent joints and wristbones.

An hour later he heard a knock at his door.

"Come in!" he snapped, without stopping.

"Mr. Roark!" gasped Mrs. Keating, staring at him from the threshold. "What on earth are you doing?"

He turned and looked at her, trying to remember who she was.

"How about the Dean?" she moaned. "The Dean that's waiting for you?"

"Oh," said Roark. "Oh, yes. I forgot."

"You . . . *forgot?*"

"Yes." There was a note of wonder in his voice, astonished by her astonishment.

"Well, all I can say," she choked, "is that it serves you right! It just serves you right! And with the commencement beginning at four-thirty, how do you expect him to have time to see you?"

"I'll go at once, Mrs. Keating."

It was not her curiosity alone that prompted her to action; it was a secret fear that the sentence of the Board might be revoked. He went to the bathroom at the end of the hall; she watched him washing his hands, throwing his loose, straight hair back into a semblance of order. He came out again, he was on his way to the stairs before she realized that he was leaving.

"Mr. Roark!" she gasped, pointing at his clothes. "You're not going like *this*?"

"Why not?"

"But it's your *Dean*!"

"Not any more, Mrs. Keating."

She thought, aghast, that he said it as if he were actually happy.

The Stanton Institute of Technology stood on a hill, its crenelated walls raised as a crown over the city stretched below. It looked like a medieval fortress, with a Gothic cathedral grafted to its belly. The fortress was eminently suited to its purpose, with stout, brick walls, a few slits wide enough for sentries, ramparts behind which defending archers could hide, and corner turrets from which boiling oil could be poured upon the attacker—should such an emergency arise in an institute of learning. The cathedral rose over it in lace splendor, a fragile defense against two great enemies: light and air.

The Dean's office looked like a chapel, a pool of dreamy twilight fed by one tall window of stained glass. The twilight flowed in through the garments of stiff saints, their arms contorted at the elbows. A red spot of light and a purple one rested respectively upon two genuine gargoyles squatting at the corners of a fireplace that had never been used. A green spot stood in the center of a picture of the Parthenon, suspended over the fireplace.

When Roark entered the office, the outlines of the Dean's figure swam dimly behind his desk, which was carved like a confessional. He was a short, plumpish gentleman whose spreading flesh was held in check by an indomitable dignity.

"Ah, yes, Roark," he smiled. "Do sit down, please."

Roark sat down. The Dean entwined his fingers on

his stomach and waited for the plea he expected. No plea came. The Dean cleared his throat.

"It will be unnecessary for me to express my regret at the unfortunate event of this morning," he began, "since I take it for granted that you have always known my sincere interest in your welfare."

"Quite unnecessary," said Roark.

The Dean looked at him dubiously, but continued:

"Needless to say, I did not vote against you. I abstained entirely. But you may be glad to know that you had quite a determined little group of defenders at the meeting. Small, but determined. Your professor of structural engineering acted quite the crusader on your behalf. So did your professor of mathematics. Unfortunately, those who felt it their duty to vote for your expulsion quite outnumbered the others. Professor Peterkin, your critic of design, made an issue of the matter. He went so far as to threaten us with his resignation unless you were expelled. You must realize that you have given Professor Peterkin great provocation."

"I do," said Roark.

"That, you see, was the trouble. I am speaking of your attitude toward the subject of architectural design. You have never given it the attention it deserves. And yet, you have been excellent in all the engineering sciences. Of course, no one denies the importance of structural engineering to a future architect, but why go to extremes? Why neglect what may be termed the artistic and inspirational side of your profession and concentrate on all those dry, technical, mathematical subjects? You intended to become an architect, not a civil engineer."

"Isn't this superfluous?" Roark asked. "It's past. There's no point in discussing my choice of subjects now."

"I am endeavoring to be helpful, Roark. You must be fair about this. You cannot say that you were not given many warnings before this happened."

"I was."

The Dean moved in his chair. Roark made him uncomfortable. Roark's eyes were fixed on him politely. The Dean thought, there's nothing wrong with the way he's looking at me, in fact it's quite correct, most properly attentive; only, it's as if I were not here.

"Every problem you were given," the Dean went on, "every project you had to design—what did you do with it? Every one of them done in that—well, I cannot call it a style—in that incredible manner of yours. It is contrary to every principle we have tried to teach you, contrary to all established precedents and traditions of Art. You may think you are what is called a modernist, but it isn't even that. It is . . . it is sheer insanity, if you don't mind."

"I don't mind."

"When you were given projects that left the choice of style up to you and you turned in one of your wild stunts—well, frankly, your teachers passed you because they did not know what to make of it. *But,* when you were given an exercise in the historical styles, a Tudor chapel or a French opera house to design—and you turned in something that looked like a lot of boxes piled together without rhyme or reason—would you say it was an answer to an assignment or plain insubordination?"

"It was insubordination," said Roark.

"We wanted to give you a chance—in view of your brilliant record in all other subjects. But when you turn in this"—the Dean slammed his fist down on a sheet spread before him—"*this* as a Renaissance villa for your final project of the year—really, my boy, it was too much!"

The sheet bore a drawing—a house of glass and concrete. In the corner there was a sharp, angular signature: Howard Roark.

"How do you expect us to pass you after this?"

"I don't."

"You left us no choice in the matter. Naturally, you would feel bitterness toward us at this moment, but . . ."

"I feel nothing of the kind," said Roark quietly. "I owe you an apology. I don't usually let things happen to me. I made a mistake this time. I shouldn't have waited for you to throw me out. I should have left long ago."

"Now, now, don't get discouraged. This is not the

right attitude to take. Particularly in view of what I am going to tell you."

The Dean smiled and leaned forward confidentially, enjoying the overture to a good deed.

"Here is the real purpose of our interview. I was anxious to let you know as soon as possible. I did not wish to leave you disheartened. Oh, I did, personally, take a chance with the President's temper when I mentioned this to him, but . . . Mind you, he did not commit himself, but . . . Here is how things stand: now that you realize how serious it is, if you take a year off, to rest, to think it over—shall we say to grow up?—there might be a chance of our taking you back. Mind you, I cannot promise anything—this is strictly unofficial—it would be most unusual, but in view of the circumstances and of your brilliant record, there might be a very good chance."

Roark smiled. It was not a happy smile, it was not a grateful one. It was a simple, easy smile and it was amused.

"I don't think you understood me," said Roark. "What made you suppose that I want to come back?"

"Eh?"

"I won't be back. I have nothing further to learn here."

"I *don't* understand you," said the Dean stiffly.

"Is there any point in explaining? It's of no interest to you any longer."

"You will kindly explain yourself."

"If you wish. I want to be an architect, not an archeologist. I see no purpose in doing Renaissance villas. Why learn to design them, when I'll never build them?"

"My dear boy, the great style of the Renaissance is far from dead. Houses of that style are being erected every day."

"They are. And they will be. But not by me."

"Come, come, now, this is childish."

"I came here to learn about building. When I was given a project, its only value to me was to learn to solve it as I would solve a real one in the future. I did them the way I'll build them. I've learned all I could learn here—in the structural sciences of which you don't approve. One more year of drawing Italian postcards would give me nothing."

An hour ago the Dean had wished that this interview would proceed as calmly as possible. Now he wished that Roark would display some emotion; it seemed unnatural for him to be so quietly natural in the circumstances.

"Do you mean to tell me that you're thinking seriously of building *that way,* when and *if* you are an architect?"

"Yes."

"My dear fellow, who will let you?"

"That's not the point. The point is, who will stop me?"

"Look here, this is serious. I am sorry that I haven't had a long, earnest talk with you much earlier . . . I know, I know, I know, don't interrupt me, you've seen a modernistic building or two, and it gave you ideas. But do you realize what a passing fancy that whole so-called modern movement is? You must learn to understand— and it has been proved by all authorities—that everything beautiful in architecture has been done already. There is a treasure mine in every style of the past. We can only choose from the great masters. Who are we to improve upon them? We can only attempt, respectfully, to repeat."

"Why?" asked Howard Roark.

No, thought the Dean, no, he hasn't said anything else; it's a perfectly innocent word; he's not threatening me.

"But it's self-evident!" said the Dean.

"Look," said Roark evenly, and pointed at the window. "Can you see the campus and the town? Do you see how many men are walking and living down there? Well, I don't give a damn what any or all of them think about architecture—or about anything else, for that matter. Why should I consider what their grandfathers thought of it?"

"That is our sacred tradition."

"Why?"

"For heaven's sake, can't you stop being so naïve about it?"

"But I don't understand. Why do you want me to think that *this* is great architecture?" He pointed to the picture of the Parthenon.

"That," said the Dean, "is the Parthenon."

"So it is."

"I haven't the time to waste on silly questions."

"All right, then." Roark got up, he took a long ruler from the desk, he walked to the picture. "Shall I tell you what's rotten about it?"

"It's the *Parthenon!*" said the Dean.

"Yes, God damn it, the Parthenon!"

The ruler struck the glass over the picture.

"Look," said Roark. "The famous flutings on the famous columns—what are they there for? To hide the joints in wood—when columns were made of wood, only there aren't, they're marble. The triglyphs, what are they? *Wood.* Wooden beams, the way they had to be laid when people began to build wooden shacks. Your Greeks took marble and they made copies of their wooden structures out of it, because others had done it that way. Then your masters of the Renaissance came along and made copies in plaster of copies in marble of copies in wood. Now here we are, making copies in steel and concrete of copies in plaster of copies in marble of copies in wood. Why?"

The Dean sat watching him curiously. Something puzzled him, not in the words, but in Roark's manner of saying them.

"Rules?" said Roark. "Here are my rules: what can be done with one substance must never be done with another. No two materials are alike. No two sites on earth are alike. No two buildings have the same purpose. The purpose, the site, the material determine the shape. Nothing can be reasonable or beautiful unless it's made by one central idea, and the idea sets every detail. A building is alive, like a man. Its integrity is to follow its own truth, its one single theme, and to serve its own single purpose. A man doesn't borrow pieces of his body. A building doesn't borrow hunks of its soul. Its maker gives it the soul and every wall, window and stairway to express it."

"But all the proper forms of expression have been discovered long ago."

"Expression—of what? The Parthenon did not serve the same purpose as its wooden ancestor. An airline terminal does not serve the same purpose as the Parthenon. Every form has its own meaning. Every man creates his meaning and form and goal. Why is it so important— what others have done? Why does it become sacred by the mere fact of not being your own? Why is anyone and everyone right—so long as it's not yourself? Why does the number of those others take the place of truth? Why is truth made a mere matter of arithmetic—and only of addition at that? Why is everything twisted out of all sense to fit everything else? There must be some reason. I don't know. I've never known it. I'd like to understand."

"For heaven's sake," said the Dean. "Sit down. . . . That's better. . . . Would you mind very much putting that ruler down? . . . Thank you. . . . Now listen to me. No one has ever denied the importance of modern technique to an architect. We must learn to adapt the beauty of the past to the needs of the present. The voice of the past is the voice of the people. Nothing has ever been invented by one man in architecture. The proper creative process is a slow, gradual, anonymous, collective one, in which each man collaborates with all the others and subordinates himself to the standards of the majority."

"But you see," said Roark quietly, "I have, let's say, sixty years to live. Most of that time will be spent working. I've chosen the work I want to do. If I find no joy in it, then I'm only condemning myself to sixty years of torture. And I can find the joy only if I do my work in the best way possible to me. But the best is a matter of standards—and I set my own standards. I inherit nothing. I stand at the end of no tradition. I may, perhaps, stand at the beginning of one."

"How old are you?" asked the Dean.

"Twenty-two," said Roark.

"Quite excusable," said the Dean; he seemed relieved. "You'll outgrow all that." He smiled. "The old standards have lived for thousands of years and nobody has been able to improve upon them. What are your modernists? A transient mode, exhibitionists trying to attract attention. Have you observed the course of their careers? Can you name one who has achieved any permanent distinction? Look at Henry Cameron. A great man, a leading architect twenty years ago. What is he today? Lucky if he gets—once a year—a garage to remodel. A bum and a drunkard, who . . ."

"We won't discuss Henry Cameron."

"Oh? Is he a friend of yours?"

"No. But I've seen his buildings."

"And you found them . . ."

"I said we won't discuss Henry Cameron."

"Very well. You must realize that I am allowing you a great deal of . . . shall we say, latitude? I am not accustomed to hold a discussion with a student who behaves in your manner. However, I am anxious to forestall, if possible, what appears to be a tragedy, the spectacle of a young man of your obvious mental gifts setting out deliberately to make a mess of his life."

The Dean wondered why he had promised the professor of mathematics to do all he could for this boy. Merely because the professor had said: "This," and pointed to Roark's project, "is a great man." A great man, thought the Dean, or a criminal. The Dean winced. He did not approve of either.

He thought of what he had heard about Roark's past. Roark's father had been a steel puddler somewhere in Ohio and had died long ago. The boy's entrance papers showed no record of nearest relatives. When asked about it, Roark had said indifferently: "I don't think I have any relatives. I may have. I don't know." He had seemed astonished that he should be expected to have any interest in the matter. He had not made or sought a single friend on the campus. He had refused to join a fraternity. He had worked his way through high school and through the three years here at the Institute. He had worked as a common laborer in the building trades since childhood. He had done plastering, plumbing, steel work, anything he could get, going from one small town to another, working his way east, to the great cities. The Dean had seen him, last summer, on his vacation, catching rivets on a skyscraper in construction in Boston; his long body relaxed under greasy overalls, only his eyes intent, and his right arm swinging forward, once in a while, expertly, without effort, to catch the flying ball of fire at the last moment, when it seemed that the hot rivet would miss the bucket and strike him in the face.

"Look here, Roark," said the Dean gently. "You have worked hard for your education. You had only one year left to go. There is something important to consider, particularly for a boy in your position. There's the *practical* side of an architect's career to think about. An architect is not an end in himself. He is only a small part of a great social whole. *Co-operation* is the key word to our modern world and to the profession of architecture in particular. Have you thought of your potential clients?"

"Yes," said Roark.

"The *Client*," said the Dean. "The Client. Think of that above all. He's the one to live in the house you build. Your only purpose is to serve him. You must aspire to give the proper artistic expression to his wishes. Isn't that all one can say on the subject?"

"Well, I could say that I must aspire to build for my client the most comfortable, the most logical, the most beautiful house that can be built. I could say that I must try to sell him the best I have and also teach him to know the best. I could say it, but I won't. Because I don't intend to build in order to serve or help anyone. I don't intend to build in order to have clients. I intend to have clients in order to build."

"How do you propose to force your ideas on them?"

"I don't propose to force or be forced. Those who want me will come to me."

Then the Dean understood what had puzzled him in Roark's manner.

"You know," he said, "you would sound much more convincing if you spoke as if you cared whether I agreed with you or not."

"That's true," said Roark. "I don't care whether you agree with me or not." He said it so simply that it did not sound offensive, it sounded like the statement of a fact which he noticed, puzzled, for the first time.

"You don't care what others think—which might be understandable. But you don't care even to make them think as you do?"

"No."

"But that's . . . that's monstrous."

"Is it? Probably. I couldn't say."

"I'm glad of this interview," said the Dean, suddenly, too loudly. "It has relieved my conscience. I believe, as others stated at the meeting, that the profession of architecture is not for you. I have tried to help you. Now I agree with the Board. You are a man not to be encouraged. You are dangerous."

"To whom?" asked Roark.

But the Dean rose, indicating that the interview was over.

Roark left the room. He walked slowly through the long halls, down the stairs, out to the lawn below. He had met many men such as the Dean; he had never understood them. He knew only that there was some important difference between his actions and theirs. It had ceased to disturb him long ago. But he always looked for a central theme in buildings and he looked for a central impulse in men. He knew the source of his actions; he could not discover theirs. He did not care. He had never learned the process of thinking about other people. But he wondered, at times, what made them such as they were. He wondered again, thinking of the Dean. There was an important secret involved somewhere in that question, he thought. There was a principle which he must discover.

But he stopped. He saw the sunlight of late afternoon, held still in the moment before it was to fade, on the gray limestone of a stringcourse running along the brick wall of the Institute building. He forgot men, the Dean and the principle behind the Dean, which he wanted to discover. He thought only of how lovely the stone looked in the fragile light and of what he could have done with that stone.

He thought of a broad sheet of paper, and he saw, rising on the paper, bare walls of gray limestone with long bands of glass, admitting the glow of the sky into the classrooms. In the corner of the sheet stood a sharp, angular signature—HOWARD ROARK.

Atlas Shrugged

Atlas Shrugged *(1957) is a mystery story, Ayn Rand once commented, "not about the murder of man's body, but about the murder—and rebirth—of man's spirit." It is the story of a man—the novel's hero—who says that he will stop the motor of the world, and does. The deterioration of the U.S. accelerates as the story progresses. Factories, farms, shops shut down or go bankrupt in ever larger numbers. Riots break out as food supplies become scarce. Is he, then, a destroyer or the greatest of liberators? Why does he have to fight his battle, not against his enemies but against those who need him most, including the woman, Dagny Taggart, a top railroad executive, whom he passionately loves? What is the world's motor—and the motive power of every man?*

Peopled by larger-than-life heroes and villains, and charged with awesome questions of good and evil, Atlas Shrugged *is a novel of tremendous scope. It presents an astounding panorama of human life—from the productive genius who becomes a worthless playboy (Francisco d'Anconia)—to the great steel industrialist who does not know that he is working for his own destruction (Hank Rearden)—to the philosopher who becomes a pirate (Ragnar Danneskjold)—to the composer who gives up his career on the night of his triumph (Richard Halley). Dramatizing AR's complete philosophy,* Atlas Shrugged *is an intellectual revolution told in the form of an action thriller of violent events—and with a ruthlessly brilliant plot and irresistible suspense.*

We do not want to spoil the plot by giving away its secret or its deeper meaning, so as a hint only we will quote here one brief exchange from the novel:

"If you saw Atlas, the giant who holds the world on his

shoulders, if you saw that he stood, blood running down his chest, his knees buckling, his arms trembling but still trying to hold the world aloft with the last of his strength, and the greater the effort the heavier the world bore down upon his shoulders—what would you tell him to do?"

"I . . . don't know. What . . . could he do? What would you tell him?"

"To shrug."

At the end of Part One, we witness the first run of the John Galt Line, Dagny Taggart's new railroad, which services the wells of oil baron Ellis Wyatt. The rail and a new bridge, both made of Rearden Metal, have been widely denounced by social critics as unsafe; the critics predict a disastrous crash when the train reaches the bridge.

The John Galt Line

Rearden was in New York on the day when Dagny telephoned him from her office. "Hank, I'm going to have a press conference tomorrow."

He laughed aloud. "No!"

"Yes." Her voice sounded earnest, but, dangerously, a bit too earnest. "The newspapers have suddenly discovered me and are asking questions. I'm going to answer them."

"Have a good time."

"I will. Are you going to be in town tomorrow? I'd like to have you in on it."

"Okay. I wouldn't want to miss it."

The reporters who came to the press conference in the office of the John Galt Line were young men who had been trained to think that their job consisted of concealing from the world the nature of its events. It was their daily duty to serve as audience for some public figure who made utterances about the public good, in phrases carefully chosen to convey no meaning. It was their daily job to sling words together in any combination they pleased, so long as the words did not fall into a sequence saying something specific. They could not understand the interview now being given to them.

Dagny Taggart sat behind her desk in an office that looked like a slum basement. She wore a dark blue suit with a white blouse, beautifully tailored, suggesting an air of formal, almost military elegance. She sat straight, and her manner was severely dignified, just a shade too dignified.

Rearden sat in a corner of the room, sprawled across a broken armchair, his long legs thrown over one of its arms, his body leaning against the other. His manner was pleasantly informal, just a bit too informal.

In the clear, monotonous voice of a military report, consulting no papers, looking straight at the men, Dagny recited the technological facts about the John Galt Line, giving exact figures on the nature of the rail, the capacity of the bridge, the method of construction, the costs. Then, in the dry tone of a banker, she explained the financial prospects of the Line and named the large profits she expected to make. "That is all," she said.

"All?" said one of the reporters. "Aren't you going to give us a message for the public?"

"That was my message."

"But hell—I mean, aren't you going to defend yourself?"

"Against what?"

"Don't you want to tell us something to justify your Line?"

"I have."

A man with a mouth shaped as a permanent sneer asked, "Well, what I want to know, as Bertram Scudder stated, is what protection do we have against your Line being no good?"

"Don't ride on it."

Another asked, "Aren't you going to tell us your motive for building that Line?"

"I have told you: the profit which I expect to make."

"Oh, Miss Taggart, don't say that!" cried a young boy. He was new, he was still honest about his job, and he felt that he liked Dagny Taggart, without knowing why. "That's the wrong thing to say. That's what they're all saying about you."

"Are they?"

"I'm sure you didn't mean it the way it sounds and . . . and I'm sure you'll want to clarify it."

"Why, yes, if you wish me to. The average profit of railroads has been two per cent of the capital invested. An industry that does so much and keeps so little, should consider itself immoral. As I have explained, the cost of the John Galt Line in relation to the traffic which it will carry makes me expect a profit of not less than fifteen per cent on our investment. Of course, any industrial profit above four per cent is considered usury nowadays. I shall, nevertheless, do my best to make the John Galt Line earn a profit of twenty per cent for me, if possible. That was my motive for building the Line. Have I made myself clear now?"

The boy was looking at her helplessly. "You don't mean, to earn a profit for *you*, Miss Taggart? You mean, for the small stockholders, of course?" he prompted hopefully.

"Why, no. I happen to be one of the largest stockholders of Taggart Transcontinental, so my share of the profits will be one of the largest. Now, Mr. Rearden is in a much more fortunate position, because he has no stockholders to share with—or would you rather make your own statement, Mr. Rearden?"

"Yes, gladly," said Rearden. "Inasmuch as the formula of Rearden Metal is my own personal secret, and in view of the fact that the Metal costs much less to produce than you boys can imagine, I expect to skin the public to the tune of a profit of twenty-five per cent in the next few years."

"What do you mean, skin the public, Mr. Rearden?" asked the boy. "If it's true, as I've read in your ads, that your Metal will last three times longer than any other and at half the price, wouldn't the public be getting a bargain?"

"Oh, have you noticed that?" said Rearden.

"Do the two of you realize you're talking for publication?" asked the man with the sneer.

"But, Mr. Hopkins," said Dagny, in polite astonishment, "is there any reason why we would talk to you, if it weren't for publication?"

"Do you want us to quote all the things you said?"

"I hope I may trust you to be sure and quote them. Would you oblige me by taking this down verbatim?" She paused to see their pencils ready, then dictated: "Miss Taggart says—quote—I expect to make a pile of money on the John Galt Line. I will have earned it. Close quote. Thank you so much."

"Any questions, gentlemen?" asked Rearden.

There were no questions.

"Now I must tell you about the opening of the John Galt Line," said Dagny. "The first train will depart from the station of Taggart Transcontinental in Cheyenne, Wyoming, at four p.m. on July twenty-second. It will be a freight special, consisting of eighty cars. It will be driven by an eight-thousand-horsepower, four-unit Diesel locomotive—which I'm leasing from Taggart Transcontinental for the occasion. It will run nonstop to Wyatt Junction, Colorado, traveling at an average speed of one hundred miles per hour. I beg your pardon?" she asked, hearing the long, low sound of a whistle.

"What did you say, Miss Taggart?"

"I said, one hundred miles per hour—grades, curves and all."

"But shouldn't you cut the speed below normal rather than . . . Miss Taggart, don't you have any consideration whatever for public opinion?"

"But I *do*. If it weren't for public opinion, an average speed of sixty-five miles per hour would have been quite sufficient."

"Who's going to run that train?"

"I had quite a bit of trouble about that. All the Taggart engineers volunteered to do it. So did the firemen, the brakemen and the conductors. We had to draw lots for every job on the train's crew. The engineer will be Pat Logan, of the Taggart Comet, the fireman—Ray McKim. I shall ride in the cab of the engine with them."

"Not really!"

"Please do attend the opening. It's on July twenty-second. The press is most eagerly invited. Contrary to my usual policy, I have become a publicity hound. Really. I should like to have spotlights, radio microphones and television cameras. I suggest that you plant a few cameras around the bridge. The collapse of the bridge would give you some interesting shots."

"Miss Taggart," asked Rearden, "why didn't you mention that I'm going to ride in that engine, too?"

She looked at him across the room, and for a moment they were alone, holding each other's glance.

"Yes, of course, Mr. Rearden," she answered.

She did not see him again until they looked at each other across the platform of the Taggart station in Cheyenne, on July 22.

She did not look for anyone when she stepped out on the platform: she felt as if her senses had merged, so that she could not distinguish the sky, the sun or the sounds of an enormous crowd, but perceived only a sensation of shock and light.

Yet he was the first person she saw, and she could not tell for how long a time he was also the only one. He stood by the engine of the John Galt train, talking to somebody outside the field of her consciousness. He was dressed in gray slacks and shirt, he looked like an expert mechanic, but he was stared at by the faces around him, because he was Hank Rearden of Rearden Steel. High above him, she saw the letters TT on the silver front of the engine. The lines of the engine slanted back, aimed at space.

There was distance and a crowd between them, but his eyes moved to her the moment she came out. They looked at each other and she knew that he felt as she did. This was not to be a solemn venture upon which their future depended, but simply their day of enjoyment. Their work was done. For the moment, there was no future. They had earned the present.

Only if one feels immensely important, she had told him, can one feel truly light. Whatever the train's run would mean to others, for the two of them their own persons were this day's sole meaning. Whatever it was that others sought in life, their right to what they now felt was all the two of them wished to find. It was as if, across the platform, they said it to each other.

Then she turned away from him.

She noticed that she, too, was being stared at, that there were people around her, that she was laughing and answering questions.

She had not expected such a large crowd. They filled the platform, the tracks, the square beyond the station; they were on the roofs of the boxcars on the sidings, at the windows of every house in sight. Something had drawn them here, something in the air which, at the last moment, had made James Taggart want to attend the opening of the John Galt Line. She had forbidden it. "If you come, Jim," she had said, "I'll have you thrown out of your own Taggart station. This is one event you're not going to see." Then she had chosen Eddie Willers to represent Taggart Transcontinental at the opening.

She looked at the crowd and she felt, simultaneously, astonishment that they should stare at her, when this event was so personally her own that no communication about it was possible, and a sense of fitness that they should be here, that they should want to see it, because the sight of an achievement was the greatest gift a human being could offer to others.

She felt no anger toward anyone on earth. The things she had endured had now receded into some outer fog, like pain that still exists, but has no power to hurt. Those things could not stand in the face of this moment's reality, the meaning of this day was as brilliantly, violently clear as the splashes of sun on the silver of the engine, all men had to perceive it now, no one could doubt it and she had no one to hate.

Eddie Willers was watching her. He stood on the platform, surrounded by Taggart executives, division heads, civic leaders, and the various local officials who had been outargued, bribed or threatened, to obtain permits to run a train through town zones at a hundred miles an hour. For once, for this day and event, his title of Vice-President was real to him and he carried it well. But while he spoke to those around him, his eyes kept following Dagny through the crowd. She was dressed in blue slacks and shirt, she was unconscious of official duties, she had left them to him, the train was now her sole concern, as if she were only a member of its crew.

She saw him, she approached, and she shook his hand;

her smile was like a summation of all the things they did not have to say. "Well, Eddie, you're Taggart Transcontinental now."

"Yes," he said solemnly, his voice low.

He watched from a distance while the train's crew was lined up in front of the engine, to face a firing squad of cameras. Dagny and Rearden were smiling, as if posing for snapshots of a summer vacation. Pat Logan, the engineer, a short, sinewy man with graying hair and a contemptuously inscrutable face, posed in a manner of amused indifference. Ray McKim, the fireman, a husky young giant, grinned with an air of embarrassment and superiority together. The rest of the crew looked as if they were about to wink at the cameras. A photographer said, laughing, "Can't you people look doomed, please? I know that's what the editor wants."

Dagny and Rearden were answering questions for the press. There was no mockery in their answers now, no bitterness. They were enjoying it. They spoke as if the questions were asked in good faith. Irresistibly, at some point which no one noticed, this became true.

"What do you expect to happen on this run?" a reporter asked one of the brakemen. "Do you think you'll get there?"

"I think we'll get there," said the brakeman, "and so do you, brother."

"Mr. Logan, do you have any children? Did you take out any extra insurance? I'm just thinking of the bridge, you know."

"Don't cross that bridge till I come to it," Pat Logan answered contemptuously.

"Mr. Rearden, how do you know that your rail will hold?"

"The man who taught people to make a printing press," said Rearden, "how did *he* know it?"

"Tell me, Miss Taggart, what's going to support a seven-thousand-ton train on a three-thousand-ton bridge?"

"My judgment," she answered.

The men of the press, who despised their own profession, did not know why they were enjoying it today. One of them, a young man with years of notorious success behind him and a cynical look of twice his age, said suddenly, "I know what I'd like to be: I wish I could be a man who covers *news!*"

The hands of the clock on the station building stood at 3:45. The crew started off toward the caboose at the distant end of the train. The movement and noise of the crowd were subsiding. Without conscious intention, people were beginning to stand still.

The dispatcher had received word from every local operator along the line of rail that wound through the mountains to the Wyatt oil fields three hundred miles away. He came out of the station building and, looking at Dagny, gave the signal for clear track ahead. Standing by the engine, Dagny raised her hand, repeating his gesture in sign of an order received and understood.

The long line of boxcars stretched off into the distance, in spaced, rectangular links, like a spinal cord. When the conductor's arm swept through the air, far at the end, she moved her arm in answering signal.

Rearden, Logan and McKim stood silently, as if at attention, letting her be first to get aboard. As she started up the rungs on the side of the engine, a reporter thought of a question he had not asked.

"Miss Taggart," he called after her, "who is John Galt?"

She turned, hanging on to a metal bar with one hand, suspended for an instant above the heads of the crowd.

"*We* are!" she answered.

Logan followed her into the cab, then McKim; Rearden went last, then the door of the engine was shut, with the tight finality of sealed metal.

The lights, hanging on a signal bridge against the sky, were green. There were green lights between the tracks, low over the ground, dropping off into the distance where the rails turned and a green light stood at the curve, against leaves of a summer green that looked as if they, too, were lights.

Two men held a white silk ribbon stretched across the track in front of the engine. They were the superintendent of the Colorado Division of Nealy's chief engineer, who had remained on the job. Eddie Willers was to cut the ribbon they held and thus to open the new line.

The photographers posed him carefully, scissors in

hand, his back to the engine. He would repeat the ceremony two or three times, they explained, to give them a choice of shots; they had a fresh bolt of ribbon ready. He was about to comply, then stopped. "No," he said suddenly. "It's not going to be a phony."

In a voice of quiet authority, the voice of a vice-president, he ordered, pointing at the cameras, "Stand back—way back. Take one shot when I cut it, then get out of the way, fast."

They obeyed, moving hastily farther down the track. There was only one minute left. Eddie turned his back to the cameras and stood between the rails, facing the engine. He held the scissors ready over the white ribbon. He took his hat off and tossed it aside. He was looking up at the engine. A faint wind stirred his blond hair. The engine was a great silver shield bearing the emblem of Nat Taggart.

Eddie Willers raised his hand as the hand of the station clock reached the instant of four.

"Open her up, Pat!" he called.

In the moment when the engine started forward, he cut the white ribbon and leaped out of the way.

From the side track, he saw the window of the cab go by and Dagny waving to him in an answering salute. Then the engine was gone, and he stood looking across at the crowded platform that kept appearing and vanishing as the freight cars clicked past him.

* * *

The green-blue rails ran to meet them, like two jets shot out of a single point beyond the curve of the earth. The crosssties melted, as they approached, into a smooth stream rolling down under the wheels. A blurred streak clung to the side of the engine, low over the ground. Trees and telegraph poles sprang into sight abruptly and went by as if jerked back. The green plains stretched past, in a leisurely flow. At the edge of the sky, a long wave of mountains reversed the movement and seemed to follow the train.

She felt no wheels under the floor. The motion was a smooth flight on a sustained impulse, as if the engine hung above the rails, riding a current. She felt no speed. It seemed strange that the green lights of the signals kept coming at them and past, every few seconds. She knew that the signal lights were spaced two miles apart.

The needle on the speedometer in front of Pat Logan stood at one hundred.

She sat in the fireman's chair and glanced across at Logan once in a while. He sat slumped forward a little, relaxed, one hand resting lightly on the throttle as if by chance; but his eyes were fixed on the track ahead. He had the ease of an expert, so confident that it seemed casual, but it was the ease of a tremendous concentration, the concentration on one's task that has the ruthlessness of an absolute. Ray McKim sat on a bench behind them. Rearden stood in the middle of the cab.

He stood, hands in pockets, feet apart, braced against the motion, looking ahead. There was nothing he could now care to see by the side of the track: he was looking at the rail.

Ownership—she thought, glancing back at him—weren't there those who knew nothing of its nature and doubted its reality? No, it was not made of papers, seals, grants and permissions. There it was—in his eyes.

The sound filling the cab seemed part of the space they were crossing. It held the low drone of the motors—the sharper clicking of the many parts that rang in varied cries of metal—and the high, thin chimes of trembling glass panes.

Things streaked past—a water tank, a tree, a shanty, a grain silo. They had a windshield-wiper motion: they were rising, describing a curve and dropping back. The telegraph wires ran a race with the train, rising and falling from pole to pole, in an even rhythm, like the cardiograph record of a steady heartbeat written across the sky.

She looked ahead, at the haze that melted rail and distance, a haze that could rip apart at any moment to some shape of disaster. She wondered why she felt safer than she had ever felt in a car behind the engine, safer here, where it seemed as if, should an obstacle rise, her breast and the glass shield would be first to smash against it. She smiled, grasping the answer: it was the security of being first, with full sight and full knowledge of one's course—not the blind sense of being pulled into the unknown by some unknown power ahead. It was the greatest sensation of existence: not to trust, but to know.

The glass sheets of the cab's windows made the spread of the fields seem vaster: the earth looked as open to movement as it was to sight. Yet nothing was distant and nothing was out of reach. She had barely grasped the sparkle of a lake ahead—and in the next instant she was beside it, then past.

It was a strange foreshortening between sight and touch, she thought, between wish and fulfillment, between—the words clicked sharply in her mind after a startled stop—between spirit and body. First, the vision—then the physical shape to express it. First, the thought—then the purposeful motion down the straight line of a single track to a chosen goal. Could one have any meaning without the other? Wasn't it evil to wish without moving—or to move without aim? Whose malevolence was it that crept through the world, struggling to break the two apart and set them against each other?

She shook her head. She did not want to think or to wonder why the world behind her was as it was. She did not care. She was flying away from it, at the rate of a hundred miles an hour. She leaned to the open window by her side, and felt the wind of the speed blowing her hair off her forehead. She lay back, conscious of nothing but the pleasure it gave her.

Yet her mind kept racing. Broken bits of thought flew past her attention, like the telegraph poles by the track. Physical pleasure?—she thought. This is a train made of steel . . . running on rails of Rearden Metal . . . moved by the energy of burning oil and electric generators . . . it's a physical sensation of physical movement through space . . . but is that the cause and the meaning of what I now feel? . . . Do they call it a low, animal joy—this feeling that I would not care if the rail did break to bits under us now—it won't—but I wouldn't care, because I have experienced this? A low, physical, material, degrading pleasure of the body?

She smiled, her eyes closed, the wind streaming through her hair.

She opened her eyes and saw that Rearden stood looking down at her. It was the same glance with which he had looked at the rail. She felt her power of volition knocked out by some single, dull blow that made her unable to move. She held his eyes, lying back in her chair, the wind pressing the thin cloth of her shirt to her body.

He looked away, and she turned again to the sight of the earth tearing open before them.

She did not want to think, but the sound of thought went on, like the drone of the motors under the sounds of the engine. She looked at the cab around her. The fine steel mesh of the ceiling, she thought, and the row of rivets in the corner, holding sheets of steel sealed together—who made them? The brute force of men's muscles? Who made it possible for four dials and three levers in front of Pat Logan to hold the incredible power of the sixteen motors behind them and deliver it to the effortless control of one man's hand?

These things and the capacity from which they came—was this the pursuit men regarded as evil? Was this what they called an ignoble concern with the physical world? Was this the state of being enslaved by matter? Was this the surrender of man's spirit to his body?

She shook her head, as if she wished she could toss the subject out of the window and let it get shattered somewhere along the track. She looked at the sun on the summer fields. She did not have to think, because these questions were only details of a truth she knew and had always known. Let them go past like the telegraph poles. The thing she knew was like the wires flying above in an unbroken line. The words for it, and for this journey, and for her feeling, and for the whole of man's earth, were: It's so simple and so right!

She looked out at the country. She had been aware for some time of the human figures that flashed with an odd regularity at the side of the track. But they went by so fast that she could not grasp their meaning until, like the squares of a movie film, brief flashes blended into a whole and she understood it. She had had the track guarded since its completion, but she had not hired the human chain she saw strung out along the right-of-way. A solitary figure stood at every mile post. Some were young schoolboys, others were so old that the silhouettes of their bodies looked bent against the sky. All of them were armed, with anything they had found, from costly rifles to ancient muskets. All of them wore railroad caps. They were the sons of Taggart employees, and old railroad men who had retired after a full lifetime of Taggart service. They had come, unsummoned, to guard this train. As the engine went past him, every man in his turn stood erect, at attention, and raised his gun in a military salute.

When she grasped it, she burst out laughing, suddenly, with the abruptness of a cry. She laughed, shaking, like a child; it sounded like sobs of deliverance. Pat Logan nodded to her with a faint smile; he had noted the guard of honor long ago. She leaned to the open window, and her arm swept in wide curves of triumph, waving to the men by the track.

On the crest of a distant hill, she saw a crowd of people, their arms swinging against the sky. The gray houses of a village were scattered through a valley below, as if dropped there once and forgotten; the roof lines slanted, sagging, and the years had washed away the color of the walls. Perhaps generations had lived there, with nothing to mark the passage of their days but the movement of the sun from east to west. Now, these men had climbed the hill to see a silver-headed comet cut through their plains like the sound of a bugle through a long weight of silence.

As houses began to come more frequently, closer to the track, she saw people at the windows, on the porches, on distant roofs. She saw crowds blocking the roads at grade crossings. The roads went sweeping past like the spokes of a fan, and she could not distinguish human figures, only their arms greeting the train like branches waving in the wind of its speed. They stood under the swinging red lights of warning signals, under the signs saying: "Stop. Look. Listen."

The station past which they flew, as they went through a town at a hundred miles an hour, was a swaying sculpture of people from platform to roof. She caught the flicker of waving arms, of hats tossed in the air, of something flung against the side of the engine, which was a bunch of flowers.

As the miles clicked past them, the towns went by, with the stations at which they did not stop, with the crowds of people who had come only to see, to cheer and to hope. She saw garlands of flowers under the sooted eaves of old station buildings, and bunting of red-white-and-blue on the time-eaten walls. It was like the pictures she had seen—and envied—in schoolbook histories of railroads, from the era when people gathered to greet the first run of a train. It was like the age when Nat Taggart moved across the country, and the stops along his way were marked by men eager for the sight of achievement. That age, she had thought, was gone; generations had passed, with no event to greet anywhere, with nothing to see but the cracks lengthening year by year on the walls built by Nat Taggart. Yet men came again, as they had come in his time, drawn by the same response.

She glanced at Rearden. He stood against the wall, unaware of the crowds, indifferent to admiration. He was watching the performance of track and train with an expert's intensity of professional interest, his bearing suggested that he would kick aside, as irrelevant, any thought such as "They like it," when the thought ringing in his mind was "It works!"

His tall figure in the single gray of slacks and shirt looked as if his body were stripped for action. The slacks stressed the long lines of his legs, the light, firm posture of standing without effort or being ready to swing forward at an instant's notice; the short sleeves stressed the gaunt strength of his arms; the open shirt bared the tight skin of his chest.

She turned away, realizing suddenly that she had been glancing back at him too often. But this day had no ties to past or future—her thoughts were cut off from implications—she saw no further meaning, only the immediate intensity of the feeling that she was imprisoned with him, sealed together in the same cube of air, the closeness of his presence underscoring her awareness of this day, as his rails underscored the flight of the train.

She turned deliberately and glanced back. He was looking at her. He did not turn away, but held her glance, coldly and with full intention. She smiled defiantly, not letting herself know the full meaning of her smile, knowing only that it was the sharpest blow she could strike at this inflexible face. She felt a sudden desire to see him trembling, to tear a cry out of him. She turned her head away, slowly, feeling a reckless amusement, wondering why she found it difficult to breathe.

She sat leaning back in her chair, looking ahead, knowing that he was as aware of her as she was of him. She found pleasure in the special self-consciousness it gave her. When she crossed her legs, when she leaned on her arm against the window sill, when she brushed her hair off her forehead—every movement of her body was underscored by a feeling the unadmitted words for which were: Is he seeing it?

The towns had been left behind. The track was rising through a country growing more grimly reluctant to permit approach. The rails kept vanishing behind curves, and the ridges of hills kept moving closer, as if the plains were being folded into pleats. The flat stone shelves of Colorado were advancing to the edge of the track—and the distant reaches of the sky were shrinking into waves of bluish mountains.

Far ahead, they saw a mist of smoke over factory chimneys—then the web of a power station and the lone needle of a steel structure. They were approaching Denver.

She glanced at Pat Logan. He was leaning forward a little farther. She saw a slight tightening in the fingers of his hand and in his eyes. He knew, as she did, the danger of crossing the city at the speed they were traveling.

It was a succession of minutes, but it hit them as a single whole. First, they saw the lone shapes, which were factories, rolling across their windowpanes—then the shapes fused into the blur of streets—then a delta of rails spread out before them, like the mouth of a funnel sucking them into the Taggart station, with nothing to protect them but the small green beads of light scattered over the ground—from the height of the cab, they saw boxcars on sidings streak past as flat ribbons of roof tops—the black hole of the train-shed flew at their faces—they hurtled through an explosion of sound, the beating of wheels against the glass panes of a vault, and the screams of cheering from a mass that swayed like a liquid in the darkness among steel columns—they flew toward a glowing arch and the green lights hanging in the open sky beyond, the green lights that were like the doorknobs of space, throwing door after door open before them. Then, vanishing behind them, went the streets clotted with traffic, the open windows bulging with human figures, the screaming sirens, and—from the top of a distant skyscraper—a cloud of paper snowflakes shimmering on the air, flung by someone who saw the passage of a silver bullet across a city stopped still to watch it.

Then they were out again, on a rocky grade—and with shocking suddenness, the mountains were before them, as if the city had flung them straight at a granite wall, and a thin ledge had caught them in time. They were clinging to the side of the vertical cliff, with the earth rolling down, dropping away, and giant tiers of twisted boulders streaming up and shutting out the sun, leaving them to speed through a bluish twilight, with no sight of soil or sky.

The curves of rail became coiling circles among walls that advanced to grind them off their sides. But the track cut through at times and the mountains parted, flaring open like two wings at the tip of the rail—one wing green, made of vertical needles, with whole pines serving as the pile of a solid carpet—the other reddish-brown, made of naked rock.

She looked down through the open window and saw the silver side of the engine hanging over empty space. Far below, the thin thread of a stream went falling from ledge to ledge, and the ferns that drooped to the water were the shimmering tops of birch trees. She saw the engine's tail of boxcars winding along the face of a granite drop—and miles of contorted stone below, she saw the coils of a green-blue rail unwinding behind the train.

A wall of rock shot upward in their path, filling the windshield, darkening the cab, so close that it seemed as if the remnant of time could not let them escape it. But she heard the screech of wheels on curve, the light came bursting back—and she saw an open stretch of rail on a narrow shelf. The shelf ended in space. The nose of the engine was aimed straight at the sky. There was nothing to stop them but two strips of green-blue metal strung in a curve along the shelf.

To take the pounding violence of sixteen motors, she thought, the thrust of seven thousand tons of steel and freight, to withstand it, grip it and swing it around a curve, was the impossible feat performed by two strips of metal no wider than her arm. What made it possible? What power had given to an unseen arrangement of molecules the power on which their lives depended and the lives of all the men who waited for the eighty box-cars? She saw a man's face and hands in the glow of a laboratory oven, over the white liquid of a sample of metal.

She felt the sweep of an emotion which she could not contain, as of something bursting upward. She turned to the door of the motor units, she threw it open to a screaming jet of sound and escaped into the pounding of the engine's heart.

For a moment, it was as if she were reduced to a single sense, the sense of hearing, and what remained of her hearing was only a long rising, falling, rising scream. She stood in a swaying, sealed chamber of metal, looking at the giant generators. She had wanted to see them, because the sense of triumph within her was bound to them, to her love for them, to the reason of the life-work she had chosen. In the abnormal clarity of a violent emotion, she felt as if she were about to grasp something she had never known and had to know. She laughed aloud, but heard no sound of it; nothing could be heard through the continuous explosion. "The John Galt Line!" she shouted, for the amusement of feeling her voice swept away from her lips.

She moved slowly along the length of the motor units, down a narrow passage between the engines and the wall. She felt the immodesty of an intruder, as if she had slipped inside a living creature, under its silver skin, and were watching its life beating in gray metal cylinders, in twisted coils, in sealed tubes, in the convulsive whirl of blades in wire cages. The enormous complexity of the shape above her was drained by invisible channels, and the violence raging within it was led to fragile needles on glass dials, to green and red beads winking on panels, to tall, thin cabinets stenciled "High Voltage."

Why had she always felt that joyous sense of confidence when looking at machines?—she thought. In these giant shapes, two aspects pertaining to the inhuman were radiantly absent: the causeless and the purposeless. Every part of the motors was an embodied answer to "Why?" and "What for?"—like the steps of a life-course chosen by the sort of mind she worshipped. The motors were a moral code cast in steel.

They *are* alive, she thought, because they are the physical shape of the action of a living power—of the mind that had been able to grasp the whole of this complexity, to set its purpose, to give it form. For an instant, it seemed to her that the motors were transparent and she was seeing the net of their nervous system. It was a net of connections, more intricate, more crucial than all of their wires and circuits: the rational connections made by that human mind which had fashioned any one part of them for the first time.

They *are* alive, she thought, but their soul operates them by remote control. Their soul is in every man who has the capacity to equal this achievement. Should the soul vanish from the earth, the motors would stop, because *that* is the power which keeps them going—not the oil under the floor under her feet, the oil that would then become primeval ooze again—not the steel cylinders that would become stains of rust on the walls of the caves of shivering savages—the power of a living mind—the power of thought and choice and purpose.

She was making her way back toward the cab feeling that she wanted to laugh, to kneel or to lift her arms, wishing she were able to release the thing she felt, knowing that it had no form of expression.

She stopped. She saw Rearden standing by the steps of the door to the cab. He was looking at her as if he knew why she had escaped and what she felt. They stood still, their bodies becoming a glance that met across a narrow passage. The beating within her was one with the beating of the motors—and she felt as if both came from him; the pounding rhythm wiped out her will. They

went back to the cab, silently, knowing that there had
been a moment which was not to be mentioned between them.

The cliffs ahead were a bright, liquid gold. Strips of
shadow were lengthening in the valleys below. The sun
was descending to the peaks in the west. They were
going west and up, toward the sun.

The sky had deepened to the greenish-blue of the
rails, when they saw smokestacks in a distant valley. It
was one of Colorado's new towns, the towns that had
grown like a radiation from the Wyatt oil fields. She saw
the angular lines of modern houses, flat roofs, great
sheets of windows. It was too far to distinguish people.
In the moment when she thought that they would not
be watching the train at that distance, a rocket shot out
from among the buildings, rose high above the town and
broke as a fountain of gold stars against the darkening
sky. Men whom she could not see, were seeing the streak
of the train on the side of the mountain, and were send-
ing a salute, a lonely plume of fire in the dusk, the symbol of celebration or of a call for help.

Beyond the next turn, in a sudden view of distance,
she saw two dots of electric light, white and red, low in
the sky. They were not airplanes—she saw the cones of
metal girders supporting them—and in the moment
when she knew that they were the derricks of Wyatt Oil,
she saw that the track was sweeping downward, that the
earth flared open, as if the mountains were flung apart—
and at the bottom, at the foot of the Wyatt hill, across
the dark crack of a canyon, she saw the bridge of Rearden Metal.

They were flying down, she forgot the careful grading,
the great curves of the gradual descent, she felt as if the
train were plunging downward, head first, she watched
the bridge growing to meet them—a small, square tunnel
of metal lace work, a few beams crisscrossed through
the air, green-blue and glowing, struck by a long ray of
sunset light from some crack in the barrier of mountains.
There were people by the bridge, the dark splash of a
crowd, but they rolled off the edge of her consciousness.
She heard the rising, accelerating sound of the wheels—
and some theme of music, heard to the rhythm of

wheels, kept tugging at her mind, growing louder—it burst suddenly within the cab, but she knew that it was only in her mind: the Fifth Concerto by Richard Halley—she thought: did he write it for this? had he known a feeling such as this?—they were going faster, they had left the ground, she thought, flung off by the mountains as by a springboard, they were now sailing through space—it's not a fair test, she thought, we're not going to touch that bridge—she saw Rearden's face above her, she held his eyes and her head leaned back, so that her face lay still on the air under his face—they heard a ringing blast of metal, they heard a drum roll under their feet, the diagonals of the bridge went smearing across the windows with the sound of a metal rod being run along the pickets of a fence—then the windows were too suddenly clear, the sweep of their downward plunge was carrying them up a hill, the derricks of Wyatt Oil were reeling before them—Pat Logan turned, glancing up at Rearden with the hint of a smile—and Rearden said, "That's that."

The sign on the edge of a roof read: Wyatt Junction. She stared, feeling that there was something odd about it, until she grasped what it was: the sign did not move. The sharpest jolt of the journey was the realization that the engine stood still.

She heard voices somewhere, she looked down and saw that there were people on the platform. Then the door of the cab was flung open, she knew that she had to be first to descend, and she stepped to the edge. For the flash of an instant, she felt the slenderness of her own body, the lightness of standing full-figure in a current of open air. She gripped the metal bars and started down the ladder. She was halfway down when she felt the palms of a man's hand slam tight against her ribs and waistline, she was torn off the steps, swung through the air and deposited on the ground. She could not believe that the young boy laughing in her face was Ellis Wyatt. The tense, scornful face she remembered, now had the purity, the eagerness, the joyous benevolence of a child in the kind of world for which he had been intended.

She was leaning against his shoulder, feeling unsteady

on the motionless ground, with his arm about her, she was laughing, she was listening to the things he said, she was answering, "But didn't you know we would?"

In a moment, she saw the faces around them. They were the bondholders of the John Galt Line, the men who were Nielsen Motors, Hammond Cars, Stockton Foundry and all the others. She shook their hands, and there were no speeches; she stood against Ellis Wyatt, sagging a little, brushing her hair away from her eyes, leaving smudges of soot on her forehead. She shook the hands of the men of the train's crew, without words, with the seal of the grins on their faces. There were flash bulbs exploding around them, and men waving to them from the riggings of the oil wells on the slopes of the mountains. Above her head, above the heads of the crowd, the letters TT on a silver shield were hit by the last ray of a sinking sun.

Ellis Wyatt had taken charge. He was leading her somewhere, the sweep of his arm cutting a path for them through the crowd, when one of the men with the cameras broke through to her side. "Miss Taggart," he called, "will you give us a message for the public?" Ellis Wyatt pointed at the long string of freight cars. "She has."

Then she was sitting in the back seat of an open car, driving up the curves of a mountain road. The man beside her was Rearden, the driver was Ellis Wyatt.

They stopped at a house that stood on the edge of a cliff, with no other habitation anywhere in sight, with the whole of the oil fields spread on the slopes below.

"Why, of course you're staying at my house overnight, both of you," said Ellis Wyatt, as they went in. "Where did you expect to stay?"

She laughed. "I don't know. I hadn't thought of it at all."

"The nearest town is an hour's drive away. That's where your crew has gone: your boys at the division point are giving a party in their honor. So is the whole town. But I told Ted Nielsen and the others that we'd have no banquets for you and no oratory. Unless you'd like it?"

"God, no!" she said. "Thanks, Ellis."

It was dark when they sat at the dinner table in a room that had large windows and a few pieces of costly furniture. The dinner was served by a silent figure in a white jacket, the only other inhabitant of the house, an elderly Indian with a stony face and a courteous manner. A few points of fire were scattered through the room, running over and out beyond the windows: the candles on the table, the lights on the derricks, and the stars.

"Do you think that you have your hands full now?" Ellis Wyatt was saying. "Just give me a year and I'll give you something to keep you busy. Two tank trains a day, Dagny? It's going to be four or six or as many as you wish me to fill." His hand swept over the lights on the mountains. "This? It's nothing, compared to what I've got coming." He pointed west. "The Buena Esperanza Pass. Five miles from here. Everybody's wondering what I'm doing with it. Oil shale. How many years ago was it that they gave up trying to get oil from shale, because it was too expensive? Well, wait till you see the process I've developed. It will be the cheapest oil ever to splash in their faces, and an unlimited supply of it, an untapped supply that will make the biggest oil pool look like a mud puddle. Did I order a pipe line? Hank, you and I will have to build pipe lines in all directions to . . . Oh, I beg your pardon. I don't believe I introduced myself when I spoke to you at the station. I haven't even told you my name."

Rearden grinned. "I've guessed it by now."

"I'm sorry, I don't like to be careless, but I was too excited."

"What were you excited about?" asked Dagny, her eyes narrowed in mockery.

Wyatt held her glance for a moment; his answer had a tone of solemn intensity strangely conveyed by a smiling voice. "About the most beautiful slap in the face I ever got and deserved."

"Do you mean, for our first meeting?"

"I mean, for our first meeting."

"Don't. You were right."

"I was. About everything but you. Dagny, to find an exception after years of . . . Oh, to hell with them! Do you want me to turn on the radio and hear what they're saying about the two of you tonight?"

"No."

"Good. I don't want to hear them. Let them swallow their own speeches. They're all climbing on the band wagon now. *We're* the band." He glanced at Rearden. "What are you smiling at?"

"I've always been curious to see what you're like."

"I've never had a chance to be what I'm like—except tonight."

"Do you live here alone, like this, miles away from everything?"

Wyatt pointed at the window. "I'm a couple of steps away from—everything."

"What about people?"

"I have guest rooms for the kind of people who come to see me on business. I want as many miles as possible between myself and all the other kinds." He leaned forward to refill their wine glasses. "Hank, why don't you move to Colorado? To hell with New York and the Eastern Seaboard! This is the capital of the Renaissance. The Second Renaissance—not of oil paintings and cathedrals—but of oil derricks, power plants, and motors made of Rearden Metal. They had the Stone Age and the Iron Age and now they're going to call it the Rearden Metal Age—because there's no limit to what your Metal has made possible."

"I'm going to buy a few square miles of Pennsylvania," said Rearden. "The ones around my mills. It would have been cheaper to build a branch here, as I wanted, but you know why I can't, and to hell with them! I'll beat them anyway. I'm going to expand the mills—and if she can give me three-day freight service to Colorado, I'll give you a race for who's going to be the capital of the Renaissance!"

"Give me a year," said Dagny, "of running trains on the John Galt Line, give me time to pull the Taggart system together—and I'll give you three-day freight service across the continent, on a Rearden Metal track from ocean to ocean!"

"Who was it that said he needed a fulcrum?" said

Ellis Wyatt. "Give me an unobstructed right-of-way and I'll show them how to move the earth!"

She wondered what it was that she liked about the sound of Wyatt's laughter. Their voices, even her own, had a tone she had never heard before. When they rose from the table, she was astonished to notice that the candles were the only illumination of the room: she had felt as if she were sitting in a violent light.

Ellis Wyatt picked up his glass, looked at their faces and said, "To the world as it seems to be right now!"

He emptied the glass with a single movement.

She heard the crash of the glass against the wall in the same instant that she saw a circling current—from the curve of his body to the sweep of his arm to the terrible violence of his hand that flung the glass across the room. It was not the conventional gesture meant as celebration, it was the gesture of a rebellious anger, the vicious gesture which is movement substituted for a scream of pain.

"Ellis," she whispered, "what's the matter?"

He turned to look at her. With the same violent suddenness, his eyes were clear, his face was calm; what frightened her was seeing him smile gently. "I'm sorry," he said. "Never mind. We'll try to think that it will last."

The earth below was streaked with moonlight, when Wyatt led them up an outside stairway to the second floor of the house, to the open gallery at the doors of the guest rooms. He wished them good night and they heard his steps descending the stairs. The moonlight seemed to drain sound as it drained color. The steps rolled into a distant past, and when they died, the silence had the quality of a solitude that had lasted for a long time, as if no person were left anywhere in reach.

She did not turn to the door of her room. He did not move. At the level of their feet, there was nothing but a thin railing and a spread of space. Angular tiers descended below, with shadows repeating the steel tracery of derricks, crisscrossing sharp, black lines on patches of glowing rock. A few lights, white and red, trembled in the clear air, like drops of rain caught on the edges of steel girders. Far in the distance, three small drops were green, strung in a line along the Taggart track. Beyond them, at the end of space, at the foot of a white curve, hung a webbed rectangle which was the bridge.

She felt a rhythm without sound or movement, a sense of beating tension, as if the wheels of the John Galt Line were still speeding on. Slowly, in answer and in resistance to an unspoken summons, she turned and looked at him.

The look she saw on his face made her know for the first time that she had known this would be the end of the journey. That look was not as men are taught to represent it, it not a matter of loose muscles, hanging lips and mindless hunger. The lines of his face were pulled tight, giving it a peculiar purity, a sharp precision of form, making it clean and young. His mouth was taut, the lips faintly drawn inward, stressing the outline of its shape. Only his eyes were blurred, their lower lids swollen and raised, their glance intent with that which resembled hatred and pain.

The shock became numbness spreading through her body—she felt a tight pressure in her throat and her stomach—she was conscious of nothing but a silent convulsion that made her unable to breathe. But what she felt, without words for it, was: Yes, Hank, yes—now—because it is part of the same battle, in some way that I can't name . . . because it is our being, against theirs . . . our great capacity, for which they torture us, the capacity of happiness . . . Now, like this, without words or questions . . . because we want it . . .

It was like an act of hatred, like the cutting blow of a lash encircling her body: she felt his arms around her, she felt her legs pulled forward against him and her chest bent back under the pressure of his, his mouth on hers.

Her hand moved from his shoulders to his waist to his legs, releasing the unconfessed desire of her every meeting with him. When she tore her mouth away from him, she was laughing soundlessly, in triumph, as if saying: Hank Rearden—the austere, unapproachable Hank Rearden of the monklike office, the business conferences, the harsh bargains—do you remember them now?—I'm thinking of it, for the pleasure of knowing that I've brought you to this. He was not smiling, his face was tight, it was the face of an enemy, he jerked her head and caught her mouth again, as if he were inflicting a wound.

She felt him trembling and she thought that this was the kind of cry she had wanted to tear from him—this surrender through the shreds of his tortured resistance. Yet she knew, at the same time, that the triumph was his, that her laughter was her tribute to him, that her defiance was submission, that the purpose of all of her violent strength was only to make his victory the greater—he was holding her body against his, as if stressing his wish to let her know that she was now only a tool for the satisfaction of his desire—and his victory, she knew, was her wish to let him reduce her to that. Whatever I am, she thought, whatever pride of person I may hold, the pride of my courage, of my work, of my mind and my freedom—*that* is what I offer you for the pleasure of your body, *that* is what I want you to use in your service—and that you want it to serve you is the greatest reward I can have.

There were lights burning in the two rooms behind them. He took her wrist and threw her inside his room, making the gesture tell her that he needed no sign of consent or resistance. He locked the door, watching her face. Standing straight, holding his glance, she extended her arm to the lamp on the table and turned out the light. He approached. He turned the light on again, with a single, contemptuous jerk of his wrist. She saw him smile for the first time, a slow, mocking, sensual smile that stressed the purpose of his action.

He was holding her half-stretched across the bed, he was tearing her clothes off, while her face was pressed against him, her mouth moving down the line of his neck, down his shoulder. She knew that every gesture of her desire for him struck him like a blow, that there was some shudder of incredulous anger within him—yet that no gesture would satisfy his greed for every evidence of her desire.

He stood looking down at her naked body, he leaned over, she heard his voice—it was more a statement of contemptuous triumph than a question: "You want it?" Her answer was more a gasp than a word, her eyes closed, her mouth open: "Yes."

She knew that what she felt with the skin of her arms was the cloth of his shirt, she knew that the lips she felt on her mouth were his, but in the rest of her there was no distinction between his being and her own, as there was no division between body and spirit. Through all the steps of the years behind them, the steps down a course chosen in the courage of a single loyalty: their love of existence—chosen in the knowledge that nothing will be given, that one must make one's own desire and every shape of its fulfillment—through the steps of shaping metal, rails and motors—they had moved by the power of the thought that one remakes the earth for one's enjoyment, that man's spirit gives meaning to insentient matter by molding it to serve one's chosen goal. The course led them to the moment when, in answer to the highest of one's values, in an admiration not to be expressed by any other form of tribute, one's spirit makes one's body become the tribute, recasting it—as proof, as sanction, as reward—into a single sensation of such intensity of joy that no other sanction of one's existence is necessary. He heard the moan of her breath; she felt the shudder of his body, in the same instant.

She looked at the glowing bands on the skin of her arm, spaced like bracelets from her wrist to her shoulder. They were strips of sunlight from the Venetian blinds on the window of an unfamiliar room. She saw a bruise above her elbow, with dark beads that had been blood. Her arm lay on the blanket that covered her body. She was aware of her legs and hips, but the rest of her body was only a sense of lightness, as if it were stretched restfully across the air in a place that looked like a cage made of sunrays.

Turning to look at him, she thought: From his aloofness, from his manner of glass-enclosed formality, from his pride in never being made to feel anything—to this, to Hank Rearden in bed beside her, after hours of a violence which they could not name now, not in words or in daylight—but which was in their eyes, as they looked at each other, which they wanted to name, to stress, to throw at each other's face.

He saw the face of a young girl, her lips suggesting a

smile, as if her natural state of relaxation were a state of radiance, a lock of hair falling across her cheek to the curve of a naked shoulder, her eyes looking at him as if she were ready to accept anything he might wish to say, as she had been ready to accept anything he had wished to do.

He reached over and moved the lock of hair from her cheek, cautiously, as if it were fragile. He held it back with his fingertips and looked at her face. Then his fingers closed suddenly in her hair and he raised the lock to his lips. The way he pressed his mouth to it was tenderness, but the way his fingers held it was despair.

He dropped back on the pillow and lay still, his eyes closed. His face seemed young, at peace. Seeing it for a moment without the reins of tension, she realized suddenly the extent of the unhappiness he had borne; but it's past now, she thought, it's over.

He got up, not looking at her. His face was blank and closed again. He picked up his clothes from the floor and proceeded to dress, standing in the middle of the room, half-turned away from her. He acted, not as if she wasn't present, but as if it did not matter that she was. His movements, as he buttoned his shirt, as he buckled the belt of his slacks, had the rapid precision of performing a duty.

She lay back on the pillow, watching him, enjoying the sight of his figure in motion. She liked the gray slacks and shirt—the expert mechanic of the John Galt Line, she thought, in the stripes of sunlight and shadow, like a convict behind bars. But they were not bars any longer, they were the cracks of a wall which the John Galt Line had broken, the advance notice of what awaited them outside, beyond the Venetian blinds—she thought of the trip back, on the new rail, with the first train from Wyatt Junction—the trip back to her office in the Taggart Building and to all the things now open for her to win—but she was free to let it wait, she did not want to think of it, she was thinking of the first touch of his mouth on hers—she was free to feel it, to hold a moment when nothing else was of any concern—she smiled defiantly at the strips of sky beyond the blinds.

"I want you to know this."

He stood by the bed, dressed, looking down at her. His voice had pronounced it evenly, with great clarity and no inflection. She looked up at him obediently. He said:

"What I feel for you is contempt. But it's nothing, compared to the contempt I feel for myself. I don't love you. I've never loved anyone. I wanted you from the first moment I saw you. I wanted you as one wants a whore—for the same reason and purpose. I spent two years damning myself, because I thought you were above a desire of this kind. You're not. You're as vile an animal as I am. I should loathe my discovering it. I don't. Yesterday, I would have killed anyone who'd tell me that you were capable of doing what I've had you do. Today, I would give my life not to let it be otherwise, not to have you be anything but the bitch you are. All the greatness that I saw in you—I would not take it in exchange for the obscenity of your talent at an animal's sensation of pleasure. We were two great beings, you and I, proud of our strength, weren't we? Well, this is all that's left of us—and I want no self-deception about it."

He spoke slowly, as if lashing himself with his words. There was no sound of emotion in his voice, only the lifeless pull of effort; it was not the tone of a man's willingness to speak, but the ugly, tortured sound of duty.

"I held it as my honor that I would never need anyone. I need you. It had been my pride that I had always acted on my convictions. I've given in to a desire which I despise. It is a desire that has reduced my mind, my will, my being, my power to exist into an abject dependence upon you—not even upon the Dagny Taggart whom I admired—but upon your body, your hands, your mouth and the few seconds of a convulsion of your muscles. I had never broken my word. Now I've broken any oath I gave for life. I had never committed an act that had to be hidden. Now I am to lie, to sneak, to hide. Whatever I wanted, I was free to proclaim it aloud and achieve it in the sight of the whole world. Now my only desire is one I loathe to name even to myself. But it is my only desire. I'm going to have you—I'd give up everything I own for it, the mills, the Metal, the achievement of my whole life. I'm going to have you at the price of more than myself: at the price of my self-esteem—and I want you to know it. I want no pretense, no evasion, no silent indulgence, with the nature of our actions left unnamed. I want no pretense about love, value, loyalty or respect. I want no shred of honor left to us, to hide behind. I've never begged for mercy. I've chosen to do this—and I'll take all the consequences, including the full recognition of my choice. It's depravity—and I accept it as such—and there is no height of virtue that I wouldn't give up for it. Now if you wish to slap my face, go ahead. I wish you would."

She had listened, sitting up straight, holding the blanket clutched at her throat to cover her body. At first, he had seen her eyes growing dark with incredulous shock. Then it seemed to him that she was listening with greater attentiveness, but seeing more than his face, even though her eyes were fixed on his. She looked as if she were studying intently some revelation that had never confronted her before. He felt as if some ray of light were growing stronger on his face, because he saw its reflection on hers, as she watched him—he saw the shock vanishing, then the wonder—he saw her face being smoothed into a strange serenity that seemed quiet and glittering at once.

When he stopped, she burst out laughing.

The shock to him was that he heard no anger in her laughter. She laughed simply, easily, in joyous amusement, in release, not as one laughs at the solution of a problem, but at the discovery that no problem had ever existed.

She threw the blanket off with a stressed, deliberate sweep of her arm. She stood up. She saw her clothes on the floor and kicked them aside. She stood facing him, naked. She said:

"I want you, Hank. I'm much more of an animal than you think. I wanted you from the first moment I saw you—and the only thing I'm ashamed of is that I did not know it. I did not know why, for two years, the brightest moments I found were the ones in your office, where I could lift my head to look up at you. I did not know the nature of what I felt in your presence, nor the reason. I know it now. That is all I want, Hank. I want you in my bed—and you are free of me for all the rest of your time. There's nothing you'll have to pretend—don't think of me, don't feel, don't care—I do not want your mind, your will, your being or your soul, so long as it's to me that you will come for that lowest one of your desires. I am an animal who wants nothing but the sensation of pleasure which you despise—but I want it from you. You'd give up any height of virtue for it while I—I haven't any to give up. There's none I seek or wish to reach. I am so low that I would exchange the greatest sight of beauty in the world for the sight of your figure in the cab of a railroad engine. And seeing it, I would not be able to see it indifferently. You don't have to fear that you're not dependent upon me. It's I who will depend on any whim of yours. You'll have me any time you wish, anywhere, on any terms. Did you call it the obscenity of my talent? It's such that it gives you a safer hold on me than on any other property you own. You may dispose of me as you please—I'm not afraid to admit it—I have nothing to protect from you and nothing to reserve. You think that this is a threat to your achievement, but it is not to mine. I will sit at my desk, and work, and when the things around me get hard to bear, I will think that for my reward I will be in your bed that night. Did you call it depravity? I am much more depraved than you are: you hold it as your guilt, and I—as my pride. I'm more proud of it than of anything I've done, more proud than of building the Line. If I'm asked to name my proudest attainment, I will say: I have slept with Hank Rearden. I had earned it."

When he threw her down on the bed, their bodies met like the two sounds that broke against each other in the air of the room: the sound of his tortured moan and of her laughter.

The Meaning of Money

The following is abridged from a speech by a copper industrialist in Atlas Shrugged, *Francisco D'Anconia, an heir to an enormous fortune.*

"So you think that money is the root of all evil?" said Francisco d'Anconia. "Have you ever asked what is the root of money? Money is a tool of exchange, which can't exist unless there are goods produced and men able to produce them. Money is the material shape of the principle that men who wish to deal with one another must deal by trade and give value for value. Money is not the tool of the moochers, who claim your product by tears, or of the looters, who take it from you by force. Money is made possible only by the men who produce. Is this what you consider evil?

"When you accept money in payment for your effort, you do so only on the conviction that you will exchange it for the product of the effort of others. It is not the moochers or the looters who give value to money. Not an ocean of tears nor all the guns in the world can transform those pieces of paper in your wallet into the bread you will need to survive tomorrow. Those pieces of paper, which should have been gold, are a token of honor—your claim upon the energy of the men who produce. Your wallet is your statement of hope that somewhere in the world around you there are men who will not default on that moral principle which is the root of money. Is this what you consider evil? . . .

"But you say that money is made by the strong at the expense of the weak? What strength do you mean? It is not the strength of guns or muscles. Wealth is the product of man's capacity to think. Then is money made by the man who invents a motor at the expense of those who did not invent it? Is money made by the intelligent at the expense of the fools? By the able at the expense of the incompetent? By the ambitious at the expense of the lazy? Money is *made*—before it can be looted or mooched—made by the effort of every honest man, each to the extent of his ability. An honest man is one who knows that he can't consume more than he has produced. . . .

"Only the man who does not need it, is fit to inherit wealth—the man who would make his own fortune no matter where he started. If an heir is equal to his money, it serves him; if not, it destroys him. But you look on and you cry that money corrupted him. Did it? Or did he corrupt his money? Do not envy a worthless heir; his wealth is not yours and you would have done no better with it. Do not think that it should have been distributed among you; loading the world with fifty parasites instead of one, would not bring back the dead virtue which was the fortune. Money is a living power that dies without its root. Money will not serve the mind that cannot match it. Is this the reason why you call it evil?

"Money is your means of survival. The verdict you pronounce upon the source of your livelihood is the verdict you pronounce upon your life. If the source is corrupt, you have damned your own existence. Did you get your money by fraud? By pandering to men's vices or men's stupidity? By catering to fools, in the hope of getting more than your ability deserves? By lowering your standards? By doing work you despise for purchasers you scorn? If so, then your money will not give you a moment's or a penny's worth of joy. Then all the things you buy will become, not a tribute to you, but a reproach; not an achievement, but a reminder of shame. Then you'll scream that money is evil. Evil, because it would not pinch-hit for your self-respect? Evil, because it would not let you enjoy your depravity? Is this the root of your hatred of money?

"Money will always remain an effect and refuse to replace you as the cause. Money is the product of virtue, but it will not give you virtue and it will not redeem your vices. Money will not give you the unearned, neither in matter nor in spirit. Is this the root of your hatred of money?

"Or did you say it's the *love* of money that's the root of all evil? To love a thing is to know and love its nature. To love money is to know and love the fact that money is the creation of the best power within you, and your passkey to trade your effort for the effort of the best among men. It's the person who would sell his soul for a nickel, who is loudest in proclaiming his hatred of money—and he has good reason to hate it. The lovers of money are willing to work for it. They know they are able to deserve it.

"Let me give you a tip on a clue to men's characters: the man who damns money has obtained it dishonorably; the man who respects it has earned it. . . .

"Then you will see the rise of the men of the double standard—the men who live by force, yet count on those who live by trade to create the value of their looted money—the men who are the hitchhikers of virtue. In a moral society, these are the criminals, and the statutes are written to protect you against them. But when a society establishes criminals-by-right and looters-by-law—men who use force to seize the wealth of *disarmed* victims—then money becomes its creators' avenger. Such looters believe it safe to rob defenseless men, once they've passed a law to disarm them. But their loot becomes the magnet for other looters, who get it from them as they got it. Then the race goes, not to the ablest at production, but to those most ruthless at brutality. When force is the standard, the murderer wins over the pickpocket. And then that society vanishes, in a spread of ruins and slaughter. . . .

"You stand in the midst of the greatest achievements of the greatest productive civilization and you wonder why it's crumbling around you, while you're damning its life-blood—money. You look upon money as the savages did before you, and you wonder why the jungle is creeping back to the edge of your cities. Throughout men's history, money was always seized by looters of one brand or another, whose names changed, but whose method remained the same: to seize wealth by force and to keep the producers bound, demeaned, defamed, deprived of honor. That phrase about the evil of money, which you mouth with such righteous recklessness, comes from a time when wealth was produced by the labor of slaves—slaves who repeated the motions once discovered by somebody's mind and left unimproved for centuries. So long as production was ruled by force, and wealth was obtained by conquest, there was little to conquer. Yet through all the centuries of stagnation and starvation, men exalted the looters, as aristocrats of the sword, as aristocrats of birth, as aristocrats of the bureau, and despised the producers, as slaves, as traders, as shopkeepers—as industrialists.

"To the glory of mankind, there was, for the first and only time in history, a *country of money*—and I have no higher, more reverent tribute to pay to America, for this means: a country of reason, justice, freedom, production, achievement. For the first time, man's mind and money were set free, and there were no fortunes-by-conquest, but only fortunes-by-work, and instead of swordsmen and slaves, there appeared the real maker of wealth, the greatest worker, the highest type of human being—the self-made man—the American industrialist."

NONFICTION SELECTIONS

The Goal of My Writing

From *The Romantic Manifesto*

The motive and purpose of my writing is *the projection of an ideal man*. The portrayal of a moral ideal, as my ultimate literary goal, as an end in itself—to which any didactic, intellectual or philosophical values contained in a novel are only the means.

Let me stress this: my purpose is *not* the philosophical enlightenment of my readers, it is *not* the beneficial influence which my novels may have on people, is it *not* the fact that my novels may help a reader's intellectual development. All these matters are important, but they are secondary considerations, they are merely consequences and effects, not first causes or prime movers. My purpose, first cause and prime mover is the portrayal of Howard Roark or John Galt or Hank Rearden or Francisco d'Anconia *as an end in himself*—not as a means to any further end. Which, incidentally, is the greatest value I could ever offer a reader.

This is why I feel a very mixed emotion—part patience, part amusement and, at times, an empty kind of weariness—when I am asked whether I am primarily a novelist or a philosopher (as if these two were antonyms), whether my stories are propaganda vehicles for ideas, whether politics or the advocacy of capitalism is my chief purpose. All such questions are so enormously irrelevant, so far beside the point, so much *not* my way of coming at things.

My way is much simpler and, simultaneously, much

more complex than that, speaking from two different aspects. The simple truth is that I approach literature as a child does: I write—and read—for the sake of the story. The complexity lies in the task of translating that attitude into adult terms.

The specific concretes, the *forms* of one's values, change with one's growth and development. The abstraction *"values"* does not. An adult's values involve the entire sphere of human activity, including philosophy—most particularly philosophy. But the basic principle—the function and meaning of values in man's life and in literature—remains the same.

My basic test for any story is: Would I want to meet these characters and observe these events in real life? Is this story an experience worth living through for its own sake? Is the pleasure of contemplating these characters an end in itself?

It's as simple as that. But that simplicity involves the total of man's existence.

It involves such questions as: What kind of men do I want to see in real life—and why? What kind of events, that is, human actions, do I want to see taking place—and why? What kind of experience do I want to live through, that is, what are my goals—and why?

It is obvious to what field of human knowledge all these questions belong: to the field of *ethics*. What is the good? What are the right actions for man to take? What are man's proper *values*?

Since my purpose is the presentation of an ideal man, I had to define and present the conditions which make him possible and which his existence requires. Since man's character is the product of his premises, I had to define and present the kind of premises and values that create the character of an ideal man and motivate his actions, which means that I had to define and present a rational code of ethics. Since man acts among and deals with other men, I had to present the kind of social system that makes it possible for ideal men to exist and to function—a free, productive, rational system, which demands and rewards the best in *every* man, great or average, and which is, obviously, laissez-faire capitalism.

But neither politics nor ethics nor philosophy are ends in themselves, neither in life nor in literature. Only Man is an end in himself.

Now observe that the practitioners of the literary school diametrically opposed to mine—the school of Naturalism—claim that a writer must reproduce what they call "real life," allegedly "as it is," exercising no selectivity and no value-judgments. By "reproduce," they mean "photograph"; by "real life," they mean whatever given concretes they happen to observe; by "as it is," they mean "as it is lived by the people around them." But observe that these Naturalists—or the good writers among them—are extremely selective in regard to two attributes of literature: *style* and *characterization*. Without selectivity, it would be impossible to achieve any sort of characterization whatever, neither of an unusual man nor of an average one who is to be offered as statistically typical of a large segment of the population. Therefore, the Naturalists' opposition to selectivity applies to only one attribute of literature: the content or *subject*. It is in regard to his choice of subject that a novelist must exercise no choice, they claim.

Why?

The Naturalists have never given an answer to that question—not a rational, logical, noncontradictory answer. Why should a writer photograph his subjects indiscriminately and unselectively? Because they "really" happened? To record what really happened is the job of a reporter or of a historian, not of a novelist. To enlighten readers and educate them? That is the job of science, not of literature, of nonfiction writing, not of fiction. To improve men's lot by exposing their misery? But *that* is a value-judgment and a moral purpose and a didactic "message"—all of which are forbidden by the Naturalist doctrine. Besides, to improve anything one must know what constitutes an improvement—and to know that, one must know what is the good and how to achieve it—and to know that, one must have a whole system of value-judgments, a system of *ethics,* which is anathema to the Naturalists.

Thus, the Naturalists' position amounts to giving a

novelist full esthetic freedom in regard to *means,* but not in regard to *ends.* He may exercise choice, creative imagination, value-judgments in regard to *how* he portrays things, but not in regard to *what* he portrays—in regard to style or characterization, but not in regard to *subject.* Man—the subject of literature—must not be viewed or portrayed selectively. Man must be accepted as the given, the unchangeable, the not-to-be-judged, the status quo. But since we observe that men do change, that they differ from one another, that they pursue different values, who, then, is to determine the human status quo? Naturalism's implicit answer is: everybody except the novelist.

The novelist—according to the Naturalist doctrine—must neither judge nor value. He is not a creator, but only a recording secretary whose master is the rest of mankind. Let others pronounce judgments, make decisions, select goals, fight over values and determine the course, the fate and the soul of man. The novelist is the only outcast and deserter of that battle. He is not to reason why—his is only to trot behind his master, note-book in hand, taking down whatever the master dictates, picking up such pearls or such swinishness as the master may choose to drop.

As far as I am concerned, I have too much self-esteem for a job of that kind.

I see the novelist as a combination of prospector and jeweler. The novelist must discover the potential, the gold mine, of man's soul, must extract the gold and then fashion as magnificent a crown as his ability and vision permit.

Just as men of ambition for material values do not rummage through city dumps, but venture out into lonely mountains in search of gold—so men of ambition for intellectual values do not sit in their backyards, but venture out in quest of the noblest, the purest, the costliest elements. I would not enjoy the spectacle of Benvenuto Cellini making mud-pies.

It is the selectivity in regard to subject—the most severely, rigorously, ruthlessly exercised selectivity—that I hold as the primary, the essential, the cardinal aspect of art. In literature, this means: *the story*—which means: the plot and the characters—which means: the kind of men and events that a writer chooses to portray.

The subject is not the only attribute of art, but it is the fundamental one, it is the end to which all the others are the means. In most esthetic theories, however, the end—the subject—is omitted from consideration, and only the means are regarded as esthetically relevant. Such theories set up a false dichotomy and claim that a slob portrayed by the technical means of a genius is preferable to a goddess portrayed by the technique of an amateur. I hold that *both* are esthetically offensive; but while the second is merely esthetic incompetence, the first is an esthetic crime.

There is no dichotomy, no necessary conflict between ends and means. The end does *not* justify the means—neither in ethics nor in esthetics. And neither do the means justify the end: there is no esthetic justification for the spectacle of Rembrandt's great artistic skill employed to portray a side of beef.

That particular painting may be taken as a symbol of everything I am opposed to in art and in literature. At the age of seven, I could not understand why anyone should wish to paint or to admire pictures of dead fish, garbage cans or fat peasant women with triple chins. Today, I understand the psychological causes of such esthetic phenomena—and the more I understand, the more I oppose them.

In art, and in literature, the end and the means, or the subject and the style, must be worthy of each other.

That which is not worth contemplating in life, is not worth re-creating in art.

Misery, disease, disaster, evil, all the negatives of human existence, are proper subjects of *study* in life, for the purpose of understanding and correcting them—but are not proper subjects of *contemplation* for contemplation's sake. In art, and in literature, these negatives are worth re-creating only in relation to some positive, as a foil, as a contrast, as a means of stressing the positive—but *not* as an end in themselves.

The "compassionate" studies of depravity which pass for literature today are the dead end and the tombstone of Naturalism. If their perpetrators still claim the justification that these things are "true" (most of them aren't)—the answer is that this sort of truth belongs in psychological case histories, not in literature. The picture of an infected ruptured appendix may be of great value in a medical textbook—but it does not belong in an art gallery. And an infected soul is a much more repulsive spectacle.

That one should wish to enjoy the contemplation of *values*, of the *good*—of man's greatness, intelligence, ability, virtue, heroism—is self-explanatory. It is the contemplation of the *evil* that requires explanation and justification; and the same goes for the contemplation of the mediocre, the undistinguished, the commonplace, the meaningless, the mindless.

At the age of seven, I refused to read the children's equivalent of Naturalistic literature—the stories about the children of the folks next door. They bored me to death. I was not interested in such people in real life; I saw no reason to find them interesting in fiction.

This is still my position today; the only difference is that today I know its full philosophical justification.

As far as literary schools are concerned, I would call myself a Romantic Realist.

Consider the significance of the fact that the Naturalists call Romantic art an "escape." Ask yourself what sort of metaphysics—what view of life—that designation confesses. An escape—from what? If the projection of value-goals—the projection of an improvement on the given, the known, the immediately available—is an "escape," then medicine is an "escape" from disease, agriculture is an "escape" from hunger, knowledge is an "escape" from ignorance, ambition is an "escape" from sloth, and life is an "escape" from death. If so, then a hard-core realist is a vermin-eaten brute who sits motionless in a mud puddle, contemplates a pigsty and whines that "such is life." If *that* is realism, then I am an escapist. So was Aristotle. So was Christopher Columbus.

There is a passage in *The Fountainhead* that deals with this issue: the passage in which Howard Roark explains to Steven Mallory why he chose him to do a statue for the Stoddard Temple. In writing that passage, I was consciously and deliberately stating the essential goal of my own work—as a kind of small, personal manifesto: "I think you're the best sculptor we've got. I think it, because your figures are not what men are, but what men could be—and should be. Because you've gone beyond the probable and made us see what is possible, but possible only through you. Because your figures are more devoid of contempt for humanity than any work I've ever seen. Because you have a magnificent respect for the human being. Because your figures are the heroic in man."

Today, more than twenty years later, I would want to change—or, rather, to clarify—only two small points. First, the words "more devoid of contempt for humanity" are not too exact grammatically; what I wanted to convey was *"untouched"* by contempt for humanity, while the work of others was touched by it to some extent. Second, the words "possible only through you" should not be taken to mean that Mallory's figures were impossible metaphysically, in realty; I meant that they were possible only because *he* had shown the way to make them possible.

"Your figures are not what men are, but what men could be—and should be."

This line will make it clear whose great philosophical principle I had accepted and was following and had been groping for, long before I heard the name "Aristotle." It was Aristotle who said that fiction is of greater philosophical importance than history, because history represents things only as they are, while fiction represents them "as they *might be* and *ought to be*."

Why must fiction represent things "as they might be and ought to be"?

My answer is contained in one statement of *Atlas Shrugged*—and in the implications of that statement: "As man is a being of self-made wealth, so he is a being of self-made soul."

Just as man's physical survival depends on his own effort, so does his psychological survival. Man faces two corollary, interdependent fields of action in which a constant exercise of choice and a constant creative process are demanded of him: the world around him and his own soul (by "soul," I mean his consciousness). Just as he has to produce the material values he needs to sustain his life, so he has to acquire the values of character that enable him to sustain it and that make his life worth living. He is born without the knowledge of either. He has to discover both—and translate them into reality—and survive by shaping the world and himself in the image of his values.

Growing from a common root, which is philosophy, man's knowledge branches out in two directions. One branch studies the physical world or the phenomena pertaining to man's physical existence; the other studies man or the phenomena pertaining to his consciousness. The first leads to abstract science, which leads to applied science or engineering, which leads to technology—to the actual production of material values. The second leads to art.

Art is the technology of the soul.

Art is the product of three philosophical disciplines: metaphysics, epistemology, ethics. Metaphysics and epistemology are the abstract base of ethics. Ethics is the applied science that defines a code of values to guide man's choice and actions—the choices and actions which determine the course of his life; ethics is the engineering that provides the principles and blueprints. Art creates the final product. It builds the model.

Let me stress this analogy: art does not *teach*—it shows, it displays the full, concretized reality of the final goal. Teaching is the task of ethics. Teaching is not the purpose of an art work, any more than it is the purpose of an airplane. Just as one can learn a great deal from an airplane by studying it or taking it apart, so one can learn a great deal from an art work—about the nature of man, of his soul, of his existence. But these are merely fringe benefits. The primary purpose of an airplane is not to *teach* man how to fly, but to give him the actual experience of flying. So is the primary purpose of an art work.

Although the representation of things "as they might be and ought to be" helps man to achieve these things in real life, this is only a secondary value. The *primary* value is that it gives him the experience of living in a world where things are *as they ought to be*. This experience is of crucial importance to him: it is his psychological life line.

Since man's ambition is unlimited, since his pursuit and achievement of values is a lifelong process—and the higher the values, the harder the struggle—man needs a moment, an hour or some period of time in which he can experience the sense of his completed task, the sense of living in a universe where his values have been successfully achieved. It is like a moment of rest, a moment to gain fuel to move farther. Art gives him that fuel. Art gives him the experience of seeing the full, immediate, concrete reality of his distant goals.

The importance of that experience is not in *what* he learns from it, but in *that* he experiences it. The fuel is not a theoretical principle, not a didactic "message," but the life-giving fact of experiencing a moment of *metaphysical* joy—a moment of love for existence.

A given individual may choose to move forward, to translate the meaning of that experience into the actual course of his own life; or he may fail to live up to it and spend the rest of his life betraying it. But whatever the case may be, the art work remains intact, an entity complete in itself, an achieved, realized, immovable fact of reality—like a beacon raised over the dark crossroads of the world, saying: "*This* is possible."

No matter what its consequences, that experience is not a way station one passes, but a stop, a value in itself. It is an experience about which one can say: "I am glad to have reached this in my life." There are not many experiences of that kind to be found in the modern world.

I have read a great many novels of which nothing remains in my mind but the dry rustle of scraps long since swept away. But the novels of Victor Hugo, and a very few others, were an unrepeatable experience to me, a beacon whose every brilliant spark is as alive as ever.

This aspect of art is difficult to communicate—it demands a great deal of the viewer or reader—but I believe that many of you will understand me introspectively.

There is a scene in *The Fountainhead* which is a direct expression of this issue. I was, in a sense, both characters in that scene, but it was written primarily from the aspect of myself as the consumer, rather than the producer, of art; it was based on my own desperate longing for the sight of human achievement. I regarded the emotional meaning of that scene as entirely personal, almost subjective—and I did not expect it to be shared by anyone. But that scene proved to be the one most widely understood and most frequently mentioned by the readers of *The Fountainhead*.

It is the opening scene of Part IV, between Howard Roark and the boy on the bicycle.

The boy thought that "man's work should be a higher step, an improvement on nature, not a degradation. He did not want to despise men; he wanted to love and admire them. But he dreaded the sight of the first house, poolroom and movie poster he would encounter on his way. . . . He had always wanted to write music, and he could give no other identity to the thing he sought. . . . Let me see that in one single act of man on earth. Let me see it made real. Let me see the answer to the promise of that music. . . . Don't work for my happiness, my brothers—show me yours—show me that it is possible— show me your achievement—and the knowledge will give me courage for mine."

This is the meaning of art in man's life.

It is from this perspective that I will now ask you to consider the meaning of Naturalism—the doctrine which proposes to confine men to the sight of slums, poolrooms, movie posters and on down, much farther down.

It is the Romantic or value-oriented vision of life that the Naturalists regard as "superficial"—and it is the vision which extends as far as the bottom of a garbage can that they regard as "profound."

It is rationality, purpose and values that they regard as naive—while sophistication, they claim, consists of discarding one's mind, rejecting goals, renouncing values and writing four-letter words on fences and sidewalks.

Scaling a mountain, they claim, is easy—but rolling in the gutter is a noteworthy achievement.

Those who seek the sight of beauty and greatness are motivated by *fear,* they claim—they who are the embodiments of chronic terror—while it takes courage to fish in cesspools.

Man's soul—they proclaim with self-righteous pride—is a sewer.

Well, they ought to know.

It is a significant commentary on the present state of our culture that I have become the object of hatred, smears, denunciations, because I am famous as virtually the only novelist who has declared that *her* soul is *not* a sewer, and neither are the souls of her characters, and neither is the soul of man.

The motive and purpose of my writing can best be summed up by saying that if a dedication page were to precede the total of my work, it would read: To the glory of Man.

And if anyone should ask me what it is that I have said to the glory of Man, I will answer only by paraphrasing Howard Roark. I will hold up a copy of *Atlas Shrugged* and say: "The explanation rests."

Man's Rights

From *The Virtue of Selfishness**

If one wishes to advocate a free society—that is, capitalism—one must realize that its indispensable foundation is the principle of individual rights. If one wishes to uphold individual rights, one must realize that capitalism is the only system that can uphold and protect them. And if one wishes to gauge the relationship of freedom to the goals of today's intellectuals, one may gauge it by the fact that the concept of individual rights is evaded, distorted, perverted and seldom discussed, most conspicuously by the so-called "conservatives."

"Rights" are a moral concept—the concept that provides a logical transition from the principles guiding an individual's actions to the principles guiding his relationship with others—the concept that preserves and protects individual morality in a social context—the link between the moral code of a man and the legal code of a society, between ethics and politics. *Individual rights are the means of subordinating society to moral law.*

Every political system is based on some code of ethics. The dominant ethics of mankind's history were variants of the altruist-collectivist doctrine which subordinated the individual to some higher authority, either mystical or social. Consequently, most political systems were variants of the same statist tyranny, differing only in degree, not in basic principle, limited only by the accidents of tradition, of chaos, of bloody strife and periodic collapse. Under all such systems, morality was a code applicable to the individual, but not to society. Society was placed

---

*This article was later reprinted in *Capitalism: The Unknown Ideal.*

65

outside the moral law, as its embodiment or source or exclusive interpreter—and the inculcation of self-sacrificial devotion to social duty was regarded as the main purpose of ethics in man's earthly existence.

Since there is no such entity as "society," since society is only a number of individual men, this meant, in practice, that the rulers of society were exempt from moral law; subject only to the traditional rituals, they held total power and exacted blind obedience—on the implicit principle of: "The good is that which is good for society (or for the tribe, the race, the nation), and the ruler's edicts are its voice on earth."

This was true of all statist systems, under all variants of the altruist-collectivist ethics, mystical or social. "The Divine Right of Kings" summarizes the political theory of the first—"*Vox populi, vox dei*" of the second. As witness: the theocracy of Egypt, with the Pharaoh as an embodied god—the unlimited majority rule or *democracy* of Athens—the welfare state run by the Emperors of Rome—the Inquisition of the late Middle Ages—the absolute monarchy of France—the welfare state of Bismarck's Prussia—the gas chambers of Nazi Germany—the slaughterhouses of the Soviet Union.

All these political systems were expressions of the altruist-collectivist ethics—and their common characteristic is the fact that society stood above the moral law, as an omnipotent, sovereign whim worshipper. Thus, politically, all these systems were variants of an *amoral* society.

The most profoundly revolutionary achievement of the United States of America was *the subordination of society to moral law*.

The principle of man's individual rights represented the extension of morality into the social system—as a limitation on the power of the state, as man's protection against the brute force of the collective, as the subordination of *might* to *right*. The United States was the first *moral* society in history.

All previous systems had regarded man as a sacrificial means to the ends of others, and society as an end in itself. The United States regarded man as an end in himself, and society as a means to the peaceful, orderly, *voluntary* co-existence of individuals. All previous systems had held that man's life belongs to society, that society can dispose of him in any way it pleases, and that any freedom he enjoys is his only by favor, by the *permission* of society, which may be revoked at any time. The United States held that man's life is his by *right* (which means: by moral principle and by his nature), that a right is the property of an individual, that society as such has no rights, and that the only moral purpose of a government is the protection of individual rights.

A "right" is a moral principle defining and sanctioning a man's freedom of action in a social context. There is only *one* fundamental right (all the others are its consequences or corollaries): a man's right to his own life. Life is a process of self-sustaining and self-generated action; the right to life means the right to engage in self-sustaining and self-generated action—which means: the freedom to take all the actions required by the nature of a rational being for the support, the furtherance, the fulfillment and the enjoyment of his own life. (Such is the meaning of the right to life, liberty, and the pursuit of happiness.)

The concept of a "right" pertains only to action—specifically, to freedom of action. It means freedom from physical compulsion, coercion or interference by other men.

Thus, for every individual, a right is the moral sanction of a *positive*—of his freedom to act on his own judgment, for his own goals, by his own *voluntary, uncoerced* choice. As to his neighbors, his rights impose no obligations on them except of a *negative* kind: to abstain from violating his rights.

The right to life is the source of all rights—and the right to property is their only implementation. Without property rights, no other rights are possible. Since man has to sustain his life by his own effort, the man who has no right to the product of his effort has no means to sustain his life. The man who produces while others dispose of his product, is a slave.

Bear in mind that the right to property is a right to action, like all the others; it is not the right *to an object,* but to the action and the consequences of producing or earning that object. It is not a guarantee that a man *will* earn any property, but only a guarantee that he will own it if he earns it. It is the right to gain, to keep, to use and to dispose of material values.

The concept of individual rights is so new in human history that most men have not grasped it fully to this day. In accordance with the two theories of ethics, the mystical or the social, some men assert that rights are a gift of God—others, that rights are a gift of society. But, in fact, the source of rights is man's nature.

The Declaration of Independence stated that men "are endowed by their Creator with certain unalienable rights." Whether one believes that man is the product of a Creator or of nature, the issue of man's opinion does not alter the fact that he is an entity of a specific kind—a rational being—that he cannot function successfully under coercion, and that rights are a necessary condition of his particular mode of survival.

"The source of man's rights is not divine law or congressional law, but the law of identity. A is A—and Man is Man. *Rights* are conditions of existence required by man's nature for his proper survival. If man is to live on earth, it is *right* for him to use his mind, it is *right* to act on his own free judgment, it is *right* to work for his values and to keep the product of his work. If life on earth is his purpose, he has a *right* to live as a rational being: nature forbids him the irrational." (*Atlas Shrugged*)

To violate man's right means to compel him to act against his own judgment, or to expropriate his values. Basically, there is only one way to do it: by the use of physical force. There are two potential violators of man's rights: the criminals and the government. The great achievement of the United States was to draw a distinction between these two—by forbidding to the second the legalized version of the activities of the first.

The Declaration of Independence laid down the principle that "to secure these rights, governments are instituted among men." This provided the only valid justification of a government and defined its only proper purpose: to protect man's rights by protecting him from physical violence.

Thus the government's function was changed from the role of ruler to the role of servant. The government was set to protect man from criminals—and the Constitution was written to protect man from the government. The Bill of Rights was not directed against private citizens, but against the government—as an explicit declaration that individual rights supersede any public or social power.

The result was the pattern of a civilized society which—for the brief span of some hundred and fifty years—America came close to achieving. A civilized society is one in which physical force is banned from human relationships—in which the government, acting as a policeman, may use force *only* in retaliation and *only* against those who initiate its use.

This was the essential meaning and intent of America's political philosophy, implicit in the principle of individual rights. But it was not formulated explicitly, nor fully accepted nor consistently practiced.

America's inner contradiction was the altruist-collectivist ethics. Altruism is incompatible with freedom, with capitalism and with individual rights. One cannot combine the pursuit of happiness with the moral status of a sacrificial animal.

It was the concept of individual rights that had given birth to a free society. It was with the destruction of individual rights that the destruction of freedom had to begin.

A collectivist tyranny dare not enslave a country by an outright confiscation of its values, material or moral. It has to be done by a process of internal corruption. Just as in the material realm the plundering of a country's wealth is accomplished by inflating the currency—so today one may witness the process of inflation being applied to the realm of rights. The process entails such a growth of newly promulgated "rights" that people do not notice the fact that the meaning of the concept is being reversed. Just as bad money drives out good money, so these "printing-press rights" negate authentic rights.

Consider the curious fact that never has there been such a proliferation, all over the world, of two contradictory phenomena: of alleged new "rights" and of slave-labor camps . . .

*   *   *

Jobs, food, clothing, recreation (!), homes, medical care, education, etc., do not grow in nature. These are man-made values—goods and services produced by men. *Who* is to provide them?

If some men are entitled *by right* to the products of the work of others, it means that those others are deprived of rights and condemned to slave labor.

Any alleged "right" of one man, which necessitates the violation of the rights of another, is not and cannot be a right.

No man can have a right to impose an unchosen obligation, an unrewarded duty or an involuntary servitude on another man. There can be no such thing as *"the right to enslave."*

A right does not include the material implementation of that right by other men; it includes only the freedom to earn that implementation by one's own effort.

Observe, in this context, the intellectual precision of the Founding Fathers: they spoke of the right to *the pursuit* of happiness—*not* of the right to happiness. It means that a man has the right to take the actions he deems necessary to achieve his happiness; it does *not* mean that others must make him happy.

The right to life means that a man has the right to support his life by his own work (on any economic level, as high as his ability will carry him); it does *not* mean that others must provide him with the necessities of life.

The right to property means that a man has the right to take the economic actions necessary to earn property, to use it and to dispose of it; it does *not* mean that others must provide him with property.

The right of free speech means that a man has the right to express his ideas without danger of suppression, interference or punitive action by the government. It does *not* mean that others must provide him with a lecture hall, a radio station or a printing press through which to express his ideas.

Any undertaking that involves more than one man, requires the *voluntary* consent of every participant. Every one of them has the *right* to make his own decision, but none has the right to force his decision on the others.

There is no such thing as "a right to a job"—there is only the right of free trade, that is: a man's right to take a job if another man chooses to hire him. There is no "right to a home," only the right of free trade: the right to build a home or to buy it. There are no "rights to a 'fair' wage or a 'fair' price" if no one chooses to pay it, to hire a man or to buy his product. There are no "rights of consumers" to milk, shoes, movies or champagne if no producers choose to manufacture such items (there is only the right to manufacture them oneself). There are no "rights" of special groups, there are no "rights of farmers, of workers, of businessmen, of employees, of employers, of the old, of the young, of the unborn." There are only *the Rights of Man*—rights possessed by every individual man and by *all* men as individuals.

Property rights and the right of free trade are man's only "economic rights" (they are, in fact, *political* rights)—and there can be no such thing as "an *economic* bill of rights." But observe that the advocates of the latter have all but destroyed the former.

Remember that rights are moral principles which define and protect a man's freedom of action, but impose no obligations on other men. Private citizens are not a threat to one another's rights or freedom. A private citizen who resorts to physical force and violates the rights of others is a criminal—and men have legal protection against him.

Criminals are a small minority in any age or country. And the harm they have done to mankind is infinitesimal when compared to the horrors—the bloodshed, the wars, the persecutions, the confiscations, the famines, the enslavements, the wholesale destructions—perpetrated by mankind's governments. Potentially, a government is the most dangerous threat to man's rights: it holds legal monopoly on the use of physical force against legally disarmed victims. When unlimited and unrestricted by individual rights, a government is man's deadliest enemy. It is not as protection against *private* actions, but against governmental actions that the Bill of Rights was written. . . .

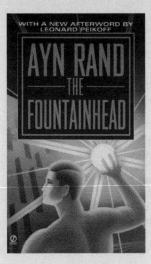

Ayn Rand's Towering Saga of a Creative Genius and His Struggle Against Those Who Would Destroy Him

SIGNET MASS MARKET
0-451-19115-3/$8.99
PLUME TRADE PAPERBACK
0-452-27333-1/$18.95
AUDIO
0-453-00911-5/$30.00

THE FOUNTAINHEAD

With over six million copies in print and more popular now than when it burst onto the scene in 1943, *The Fountainhead* is Ayn Rand's groundbreaking novel about the fate of one man's artistic and moral integrity in the face of relentless pressures to compromise and conform. Through the story of architectural genius Howard Roark, his struggles against successful rival Peter Keating, and his explosive love affair with a beautiful woman who tries to destroy him, Ayn Rand explores the theme of the independent individual who remains true to his ideals in a society driven by envy, compromise, and the herd instinct.

This edition contains a special afterword by Rand's literary executor Leonard Peikoff, which includes excerpts from Ayn Rand's own notes on the making of *The Fountainhead,* the novel that vaulted her to extraordinary and enduring success and continues to draw a worldwide audience to her work.

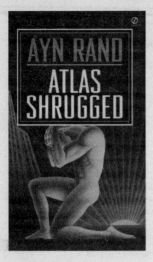

Ayn Rand's Magnum Opus—The Most Challenging Bestseller, Intellectually and Morally, of Our Time

SIGNET MASS MARKET
0-451-19114-5/$8.99
PLUME TRADE PAPERBACK
0-452-01187-6/$17.95
AUDIO
1-565-11127-3
(Abridged)/$30.00
1-565-11417-5
(Unabridged)/$49.95

ATLAS SHRUGGED

First published in 1957 and a perennial bestseller for over four decades, *Atlas Shrugged* is Ayn Rand's masterpiece, a moral and intellectual thriller, a novel that grapples with the grand questions of good and evil, and offers the most complete statement of the author's own philosophy, Objectivism. Through a wide range of larger-than-life characters such as Dagny Taggart and John Galt, along with their villainous counterparts, Rand vividly dramatizes the opposition between thought and faith, between egoism and altruism, between the individual and the state.

As relevant today as when it first appeared, *Atlas Shrugged* continues to rank as one of the 20th century's most influential books as scores of new readers find their own questions and dilemmas, their own aspirations and ideals, reflected in its pages.

Ayn Rand's Creative
Projection of a Future
Devoid of Individual
Creativity

SIGNET MASS MARKET
0-451-19113-7/$7.99
PLUME TRADE PAPERBACK
0-452-28125-3/$13.95

ANTHEM
Expanded 50th Anniversary Edition

The first of her three bestselling novels and a clear predecessor to *The Fountainhead* and *Atlas Shrugged*, *Anthem* remains one of Ayn Rand's most beloved and widely read works. Set in a terrifying future in which all people live in collectives and all expressions of individualism have been suppressed—a world where even the word "I" has been banished—this gripping story explores the spark of freedom and courage that remain in the one man willing to stand against the rulers and choose for himself.

   This edition includes an introduction by Leonard Peikoff and an appendix containing a facsimile of the original English edition, published in 1938, with Rand's revisions for the 1946 American edition written in her own hand. These revisions offer admirers of Rand's prose style and all those interested in her literary development a fascinating look at how the author worked.

THE ART OF NONFICTION
A Guide for Writers and Readers
Edited by Robert Mayhew, Ph.D.
Introduction by Peter Schwartz

In these edited transcripts of a series of sixteen informal lectures delivered in the late 1960s, Ayn Rand gives clear and genuinely helpful guidance to beginning nonfiction writers while providing readers with a fascinating discourse on art and creation. Based on the idea that writing nonfiction is a rational skill that can be learned like any other, Rand takes readers through the writing process step by step, from choosing a subject to polishing a draft to mastering an individual style. She also explores larger issues, including the psychological aspects of writing and the different roles played by the conscious and subconscious mind.

Geared to both authors of theoretical works and to those interested in journalistic writing, *The Art of Nonfiction* offers a wealth of insight from one of the masters of the genre.

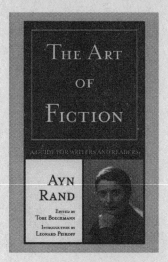

Ayn Rand's Expert
Guidance on All
Aspects of Reading
and Writing Fiction

PLUME TRADE PAPERBACK
0-425-28154-7/$12.95

THE ART OF FICTION
A Guide for Writers and Readers
Edited by Tore Boeckmann

Based on an extraordinary series of informal lectures Ayn Rand gave to a group of friends in her own living room, *The Art of Fiction* offers penetrating insight and specific guidance on all aspects of writing and reading fiction. Rand gave these talks—speaking extemporaneously from just a few notes—in 1958, a year after she'd published *Atlas Shrugged*, at the height of her creative powers. Supplying practical advice on everything from theme, plot, and characterization to the role of the subconscious and issues of style, Rand ranges widely, using examples from her own work and providing incisive—sometimes devastating—analyses of fellow writers such as Thomas Wolfe, Sinclair Lewis, Victor Hugo, and others. Accessible, inspiring, and always to-the-point, *The Art of Fiction* shares the techniques and values that made one of the 20th century's greatest writers.

SIGNET MASS MARKET
0-451-14607-7/$7.99

THE EARLY AYN RAND
Edited and with an introduction and notes by Leonard Piekoff

Selected by Leonard Peikoff, this collection of eleven pieces of Ayn Rand's previously unpublished short fiction ranges from beginner's exercises to unknown plays to excerpts from early versions of *We the Living* and *The Fountainhead*. Arranged chronologically, from 1926 through the thirties, these pieces allow readers to follow the extraordinary trajectory of Rand's literary and intellectual growth, from a 21-year-old Russian immigrant struggling to master English to the brilliant prose stylist she was to become in her mature work.

SIGNET MASS MARKET
0-451-18784-9/$7.99

WE THE LIVING

We the Living is Ayn Rand's first and most personal novel, a work which is "as near to an autobiography as I will ever write." Published in 1936 and set against the background of the Russian Revolution, *We the Living* tells the story of three people who see through the lies of socialist slogans, defy the power of the state, and demand to live their own lives and pursue their own happiness. Fans of Rand's later work will want to read the book that began her remarkable career and introduced the major themes she would elaborate in her subsequent writings.

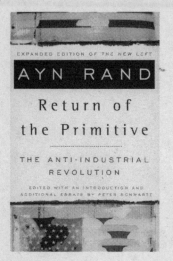

MERIDIAN TRADE PAPERBACK
0-452-01184-1/$14.95

RETURN OF THE PRIMITIVE
The Anti-Industrial Revolution
Edited and with an introduction and additional essays by Peter Schwartz

First published in 1971 under the title *The New Left* and now edited and expanded by Peter Schwartz, *Return of the Primitive* brings together fifteen of Ayn Rand's incisive political essays. These essays cover Rand's profound attacks on the student radicalism of the sixties, on what she termed the "anti-industrial revolution," and on the ideological precursors of the political correctness and multiculturalism that flourish on today's college campuses. Her perceptive warnings are as relevant now as when she made them thirty years ago.

PLUME TRADE PAPERBACK
0-452-27887-2/$18.95

JOURNALS OF AYN RAND
Edited by David Harriman

Including detailed notes on her three most important
novels—*The Fountainhead, Atlas Shrugged,* and *We the
Living*—along with her first philosophical musings, a passionate essay defending the House Un-American Activities Committee, plans for her last projected novel, and
much more, these entries offer a fascinating behind-the-
scenes glimpse into the life and work of Ayn Rand. Containing much new material—writing that Rand showed
to virtually no one during her lifetime—this volume is
essential reading for all Ayn Rand aficionados.

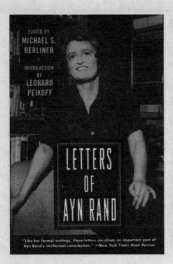

"Like her formal writings, these letters constitute an important part of
Ayn Rand's intellectual contribution." —*New York Times Book Review*

PLUME TRADE PAPERBACK
0-452-27404-4/$17.95

LETTERS OF AYN RAND
Edited by Michael S. Berliner

Covering a span of over five decades, these extraordinary letters reveal more about Ayn Rand's own life than
anything else she wrote. They range from a 1926 letter
to a Russian "Leo" expressing her wide-eyed love for
America, to correspondence about her early struggles as
a screenwriter, to letters indicating her astonishing success both as author and as founder of a new philosophy,
Objectivism. Written to answer unknown fans, and also
to such eminent contemporaries as Cecil B. DeMille,
Frank Lloyd Wright, and H. L. Mencken, along with
love notes to her husband Frank O'Connor, these letters
offer a wealth of insight into Ayn Rand the person.

PLUME TRADE PAPERBACK
0-452-28040-0/$16.95

THE AYN RAND READER
Edited by Gary Hull and Leonard Peikoff

The Ayn Rand Reader provides a convenient and easily accessible sampling of the author's most important ideas and works. Including excerpts from her four novels; non-fiction denunciations of the mysticism, altruism, and collectivism she saw as threatening the freedom of the individual; and essays setting out her basic philosophical, aesthetic, and political positions, this *Reader* supplies Ayn Rand admirers and newcomers alike with a wonderful distillation of her wide-ranging intelligence.

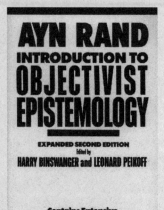

MERIDIAN TRADE PAPERBACK
0-452-01030-6/$17.95

INTRODUCTION TO OBJECTIVIST EPISTEMOLOGY
Expanded Second Edition
Edited by Harry Binswanger and Leonard Peikoff

In this eloquent analysis and defense of reason and man's conceptual faculty, Ayn Rand mounts a powerful counterattack against those who would tell us that logic is arbitrary, and reality merely a social construct. This second edition of Rand's philosophical masterwork includes never-before-published excerpts from workshops Rand conducted between 1969 and 1971. Here we see Rand—arguing, debating and clarifying her ideas, which offers the reader the inspiring spectacle of her unique mind in action.

MERIDIAN TRADE PAPERBACK
0-452-01046-21/$15.95

THE VOICE OF REASON
Essays in Objectivist Thought
Edited and with additional essays by Leonard Peikoff

The Voice of Reason brings together, for the first time in book form, twenty-six essays written in the final years of Ayn Rand's life and covering such varied subjects as education, psychology, Vietnam, socialized medicine, women in politics, global Balkanization, and many others. This edition includes five additional essays by Leonard Peikoff, Rand's longtime associate and literary executor, and concludes with Peikoff's epilogue, "My Thirty Years With Ayn Rand," which provides readers with a glimpse into what Ayn Rand was like as a person and as a friend.

MERIDIAN TRADE PAPERBACK
0-452-01051-9/$17.95

THE AYN RAND LEXICON
Objectivism From A to Z
Edited by Harry Binswanger

Organized alphabetically by subject and drawn from
Ayn Rand's many articles, lectures, and books, *The Ayn
Rand Lexicon* presents the Objectivist view on over 400
topics in philosophy, politics, art, economics, and psychology. This remarkably comprehensive and convenient
sourcebook allows readers to zero in on any subject
about which Rand wrote without having to search
through her voluminous writings. Essential for Rand en-
thusiasts and newcomers alike, *The Ayn Rand Lexicon*
offers her most important ideas in their most succinct
and accessible form.

SIGNET MASS MARKET
0-451-14916-5/$6.99

THE ROMANTIC MANIFESTO

Here is Ayn Rand's boldly original assessment of what art is—and of the standards by which an art work should be judged. Dispersing the mits that obscure esthetic judgments, she offers a precise definition of art, and presents a devastating critique of both Naturalistic and modern art. In elaborating the goal of her own writing—the portrayal of the ideal man—Rand gives readers invaluable insight into how she approached her own novels and why they achieve such power.

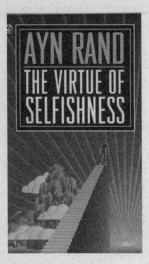

SIGNET MASS MARKET
0-451-16393-1/$7.99

THE VIRTUE OF SELFISHNESS

The Virtue of Selfishness is the seminal statement of Ayn Rand's code of morality: the ethics of rational self inter- est. Whereas altruism is incompatible with human na- ture—and leads ultimately to dictatorship—a free society, she holds, depends upon the selfishness of the individual. Rand returns to the true meaning of selfish- ness—and uses this concept to clarify a wide range of social and ethical issues, from man's rights to the psy- chology of pleasure to the nature of government.

SIGNET MASS MARKET
0-451-16308-7/$7.99

FOR THE NEW INTELLECTUAL

Containing the main philosophical passages from Ayn Rand's novels, in addition to the lengthy title essay, which presents an historical overview of Western philosophy and civilization, *For the New Intellectual* offers an alternative to the cynicism and despair of the modern age. Rand argues that only the acceptance of reason as an absolute—along with a return to pure capitalism—can save the West from collapse; and that there is still time to do it.

SIGNET MASS MARKET
0-451-14795-2/$7.99

CAPITALISM: THE UNKNOWN IDEAL

This collection of twenty-four essays, with contributions by Alan Greenspan, and others, sets forth Ayn Rand's defense of capitalism not only as a practical economic system but as the embodiment and protector of man's highest moral-philosophical ideals which have yet to be fully realized. Covering such topics as the persecution of big business, the evils of government controls, the danger of rule by consensus, the roots of war, and many others, *Capitalism: The Unknown Ideal* offers the most comprehensive statement of Ayn Rand's compelling political vision.

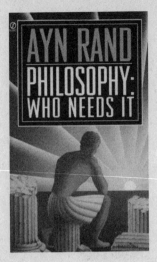

SIGNET MASS MARKET
0-451-13893-7/$7.99

PHILOSOPHY: WHO NEEDS IT

Ayn Rand holds that everybody needs philosophy. Philosophy, she says, is not some academic discipline removed from life, but a powerful force that underlies every human decision and action. The choice is not whether to have a philosophy but whether to have a rational known one and live accordingly or to be driven willy-nilly by a random smattering of unexamined and unidentified notions. In his lucid book, Rand helps readers see just how essential philosophy is for everyday life.

PLUME TRADE PAPERBACK
0-452-26486-3/$10.95

NIGHT OF JANUARY 16th

In this compelling and innovative courtroom drama, which Ayn Rand described as "a murder trial without a pre-arranged verdict," the jurors are selected from the audience and must decide whether or not Karen Andre, secretary and mistress to Sweden's great financier Bjorn Faulkner, is guilty of his murder. Dramatizing the theme that pervades Ayn Rand's work—the individualist against the conformist—*Night of January 16th* has achieved worldwide popularity and acclaim since its original Broadway success.

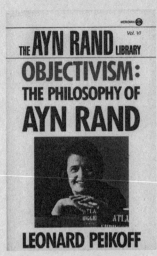

An Essential Work by
Leonard Peikoff, Ayn
Rand's Literary
Executor and the
World's Premier Ayn
Rand Scholar

MERIDIAN TRADE PAPERBACK
0-452-01101-9/$16.95

OBJECTIVISM:
THE PHILOSOPHY OF AYN RAND
Leonard Peikoff

Based on a lecture course given in 1976 and endorsed
by Ayn Rand as "the only authorized presentation of the
entire theoretical structure of Objectivism," this volume
offers the definitive statement of Rand's philosophy. Dr.
Peikoff covers every topic Ayn Rand considered important—from sense perception, free will, and reason, to
sex, capitalism, art, and much more. The book includes
abundant material, never-before-published, taken from
Piekoff's private conversations with Rand across three
decades. For anyone who wishes to grasp fully Ayn
Rand's philosophy, here is the invaluable guide.

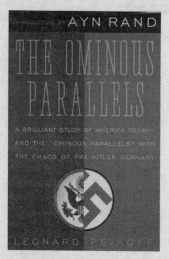

PLUME TRADE PAPERBACK
0-452-01117-5/$15.00

THE OMINOUS PARALLELS
Leonard Peikoff
Introduction by Ayn Rand

In this brilliant study, Leonard Peikoff, Ayn Rand's successor as the spokesman for Objectivism, reveals the frightening similarities between the United States today and pre-Nazi Germany. Self-sacrifice in favor of the group, Oriental mysticism, radical "truth," progressive education, an ever growing state—these are some of the ideas and trends that Peikoff dissects, exposing the kind of philosophy they symbolize and showing how they parallel the thinking that led Hitler Germany. A book which Ayn Rand herself described as "protection and ammunition" against "today's philosophical bankruptcy," *The Ominous Parallels* is a clarion call to all those concerned with preserving the rights of Americans—and of man.

A BRIEF BIOGRAPHY OF AYN RAND

Ayn Rand was born in St. Petersburg, Russia, on February 2, 1905. At the age of nine, she decided to make fiction-writing her career. In late 1925 she obtained permission to leave the USSR for a visit to relatives in the United States. Arriving in New York in February 1926, she first spent six months with her relatives in Chicago before moving to Los Angeles.

On her second day in Hollywood, the famous director Cecil B. DeMille noticed her standing at the gate of his studio, offered her a ride to the set of his silent movie *The King of Kings,* and gave her a job, first as an extra and later as a script reader. During the next week at the studio, she met an actor, Frank O'Connor, whom she married in 1929; they were happily married until his death fifty years later.

After struggling for several years at various menial jobs, including one in the wardrobe department at RKO, she sold her first screenplay, "Red Pawn," to Universal Studios in 1932 and then saw her first play, *Night of January 16th,* produced in Hollywood and (in 1935) on Broadway. In 1936, her first novel, *We the Living,* was published.

She began writing *The Fountainhead* in 1935. In the character of Howard Roark, she presented for the first time the Ayn Rand hero, whose depiction was the chief goal of her writing: the ideal man, man as "he could be and ought to be." *The Fountainhead* was rejected by a dozen publishers but finally accepted by Bobbs-Merrill; it came out in 1943. The novel made publishing history by becoming a bestseller within two years purely through word of mouth; it gained lasting recognition for AR as a champion of individualism.

Atlas Shrugged (1957) was her greatest achievement and last work of fiction. In this novel she dramatizes her unique philosophy of Objectivism in an intellectual mystery story that integrates ethics, metaphysics, epistemology, politics, economics, and sex. Although she considered herself primarily a fiction writer, she realized early that in order to create heroic characters, she had to identify the philosophic principles which make such people possible. She proceeded to develop a "philosophy for living on earth." Objectivism has now gained a worldwide audience and is an ever growing presence in American culture. Her novels continue to sell in enormous numbers every year, proving themselves enduring classics of literature.

Ayn Rand died on March 6, 1982, at her home in New York City.

RECOLLECTIONS OF AYN RAND:

A CONVERSATION WITH LEONARD PEIKOFF, Ph.D., AYN
RAND'S LONGTIME ASSOCIATE AND INTELLECTUAL HEIR

*Dr. Peikoff, you met Miss Rand when you were seventeen
and were associated with her until her death, thirty-one
years later. What were your first impressions of her? What
was she like?*

The strongest first impression I had of her was her pas-
sion for ideas. Ayn Rand was unlike anyone I had ever
imagined. Her mind was utterly first-handed: she said
what no one else had ever said or probably ever thought,
but she said these things so logically—so simply, factu-
ally, persuasively—that they seemed to be self-evident.
She radiated the kind of intensity that one could imagine
changing the course of history. Her brilliantly perceptive
eyes looked straight at you and missed nothing: neither
did her methodical, painstaking, virtually scientific re-
plies to my questions miss anything. She made me think
for the first time that thinking is important. I said to
myself after I left her home: "All of life will be different
now. If she exists, everything is possible."

*In her fiction, Ayn Rand presented larger-than-life
heroes—embodiments of her philosophy of rational egoism—that have inspired countless readers over the years.
Was Ayn Rand's own life like that of her characters? Did
she practice her own ideals?*

Yes, always. From the age of nine, when she decided on
a career as a writer, everything she did was integrated
toward her creative purpose. As with Howard Roark,

dedication to thought and thus to her work was the root
of Ayn Rand's person.

In every aspect of life, she once told me, a man should
have favorites. He should define what he likes or wants
most and why, and then proceed to get it. She always did
just that—fleeing the Soviet dictatorship for America,
tripping her future husband on a movie set to get him
to notice her, ransacking ancient record shops to unearth
some lost treasure, even decorating her apartment with
an abundance of her favorite color, blue-green.

*Given her radical views in morality and politics, did she
ever soften or compromise her message?*

Never. She took on the whole world—liberals, conservatives, communists, religionists, Babbitts and avant-garde
alike—but opposition had no power to sway her from
her convictions.

I never saw her adapting her personality or viewpoint
to please another individual. She was always the same
and always herself, whether she was talking with me
alone, or attending a cocktail party of celebrities, or
being cheered or booed by a hall full of college students,
or being interviewed on national television.

Couldn't she have profited by toning things down a little?

She could never be tempted to betray her convictions.
A Texas oil man once offered her up to a million dollars
to use in spreading her philosophy, if she would only
add a religious element to it to make it more popular.
She threw his proposal into the wastebasket. "What
would I do with his money," she asked me indignantly,
"if I have to give up my mind in order to get it?"

Her integrity was the result of her method of thinking
and her conviction that ideas really matter. She knew
too clearly how she had reached her ideas, why they
were true, and what their opposites were doing to
mankind.

Who are some writers that Ayn Rand respected and enjoyed reading?

She did not care for most contemporary writers. Her favorites were the nineteenth-century Romantic novelists. Above all, she admired Victor Hugo, though she often disagreed with his explicit views. She liked Dostoyevsky for his superb mastery of plot structure and characterization, although she had no patience for his religiosity. In popular literature, she read all of Agatha Christie twice, and also liked the early novels of Mickey Spillane.

In addition to writing bestsellers, Ayn Rand originated a distinctive philosophy of reason. If someone wants to get an insight into her intellectual and creative development, what would you suggest?

A reader ought first to read her novels and main nonfiction in order to understand her views and values. Then, to trace her early literary development, a reader could pick up *The Early Ayn Rand,* a volume I edited after her death. It features a selection of short stories and plays that she wrote while mastering English and the art of fiction-writing. For a glimpse of her lifelong intellectual development, I would recommend the recent book *Journals of Ayn Rand,* edited by David Harriman.

Ayn Rand's life was punctuated by disappointments with people, frustration, and early poverty. Was she embittered? Did she achieve happiness in her own life?

She did achieve happiness. Whatever her disappointments or frustrations, they went down, as she said about Roark, only to a certain point. Beneath it was her self-esteem, her values, and her conviction that happiness, not pain, is what matters. I remember a spring day in 1957. She and I were walking up Madison Avenue in New York toward the office of Random House, which was in the process of bringing out *Atlas Shrugged.* She was looking at the city she had always loved most, and now, after decades of rejection, she had seen the top publishers in that city competing for what she knew, triumphantly, was her masterpiece. She turned to me suddenly and said: "Don't ever give up what you want in life. The struggle is worth it." I never forgot that. I can still see the look of quiet radiance on her face.

AYN RAND ESSAY CONTESTS

Each year the Ayn Rand Institute sponsors high school essay contests on Ayn Rand's novels *Anthem* and *The Fountainhead.* Contests on Ayn Rand's novels have been held annually by the Institute since 1985, and have attracted more than 95,000 participants. Today more than 9,000 students participate annually.

The Institute awards a total of $62,000 to 502 of the top entrants in the contests. The top prize for *The Fountainhead* is $10,000. All awards are cash prizes, with no strings on how the prize money is spent. All 9th and 10th grade students are eligible for the *Anthem* contest, and all 11th and 12th grade students are eligible for *The Fountainhead* contest. Students must read the novel for the contest they are eligible to enter and write an essay on one of three topics provided by the Institute

The Institute now also sponsors an essay contest for college students on Ayn Rand's novel *Atlas Shrugged.* Complete information on all three contests is available on the Institute Web site at http://www.aynrand.org/contests/. Information and materials for teaching the novels is also available on this Web site.

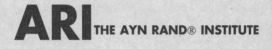